FRANÇOIS, PORTRAIT OF AN ABSENT FRIEND

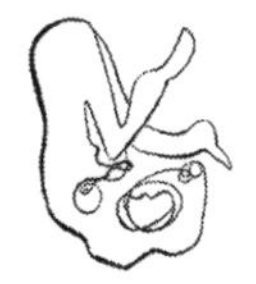

Michaël Ferrier is a Franco-Mauritian writer, novelist and essayist, Professor at Chuo University in Tokyo (Japan), and Director of the Research Group *Figures de l'étranger*. He is the author of several texts on Japanese culture and is also the author of several novels. Ferrier has won several literary prizes: the Asia Literary Prize in 2005, the Golden Door Prize in 2010, the Édouard Glissant Prize in 2012 (for *Fukushima, récit d'un désastre*), the Franz Hessel Prize for Contemporary Literature in 2015, and the Prix Décembre, one of France's premier literary awards, in 2018.

Martin Munro is Winthrop-King Professor of French and Francophone Studies at Florida State University. He previously worked in Scotland, Ireland, and Trinidad. In 2019, he published a translation of Michaël Ferrier's *Mémoires d'outre mer* and in 2022 a translation of Ferrier's *Scrabble*. In 2020-21 he was a Fellow at the National Humanities Center in North Carolina. His latest book is *Listening to the Caribbean: Sounds of Slavery, Revolt, and Race* (Liverpool, 2022). He is Director of the Winthrop-King Institute for Contemporary French and Francophone Studies at Florida State

This translation has been published in Great Britain
by Fum d'Estampa Press Limited 2023
001

Set in Minion Pro

Printed and bound by Great Britain by CMP UK Ltd.
A CIP catalogue record for this book is available from the British Library

ISBN: 978-1-913744-22-9

FRANÇOIS, PORTRAIT OF AN ABSENT FRIEND

MICHAËL FERRIER

Translated by

MARTIN MUNRO

FRANÇOIS, PORTRAIT OF AN ABSENT FRIEND

For Sylvia

We have a treasure without end
If we but have the shadow of a friend.
MENANDER

When two friends live in harmony, they create a music.
MATTEO RICCI

On Friendship

It comes like a wave.

That night, I understood what a blank voice was. Jérôme's voice was blank.

Now, the memories come flooding. It comes like a wave.

The voice is blank and the bedroom is black. The house sleeps in the December cold. The Tokyo winter is always dry and cold: it won't protect you. The telephone rings. Death often appears like that, in the middle of the night. It is a howling, or a call. The illuminated screen tells me it is Jérôme and that he is calling from Paris, but the voice at the end of the line does not seem to belong to anyone or to be connected to anything. The voice is strange, not completely calm, though it keeps calm, which is not the same thing. It is grappling with something immense and deep—something like a tidal wave. Then Jérôme announces the news to me. He tells me softly, almost delicately, as if he were placing a cover over a body, as if he were unfolding a sheet: François died tonight, he drowned in the sea around the island of Graciosa, off the coast of the Canaries. And then the other piece of news straight after, the same one, another, I no longer know. Because there was something worse, if that was possible: François did not die alone; his little daughter, Bahia, died with him. Both were carried away, swallowed up by the wave—Sylvia remained alone, abandoned on the shore. It comes like a wave.

Jérôme, my friend since adolescence, just like François. He now manages a major evening newspaper, the "daily paper of reference" as it is known: he is not therefore the type to lose his composure, but in this case, there is no way to stop it. Choking with emotion, nothing comes out except the icy trickle of his voice. He'd called me right away and I thank him silently, I don't know how he found the courage to do it, to announce the news to me in the most careful, the most gentle way possible, with a sense of correctness that is all his own.

But that voice, my goodness, it had something in it I have never heard before... Every disaster has its own timbre, an acoustics of distress. Even with the thousands of kilometers that separate us, I feel *physically* a great violence, the pressure he feels at the other end of the world, pushing down on his rib cage. Normally, Jérôme's voice is calm, poised: the measured diphthongs, the fullness of his consonants, the breathy nasal sounds, the whole range of his voice unfolds in an amiable, conciliatory tone, with the polish of a great journalist used to managing the turbulences of the world. It is the voice of an alto, soft and full: it rarely swells up, and it is never forced. There are very few sudden movements in his voice: its vitality never becomes fierceness, and he never tries to give to it an agreeable inflexion or calculated ambiguity. Emptied of all hardness, it even takes on a slight Ollioules accent at the end of a sentence like a sprig of thyme, which lends a particular flavor and a great sense of lightness.

But today, François has died. "François is dead," he says, and Jérôme's voice dies with him. Now it is a toneless voice, without any specific qualities, a voice haunted by absence.

Without pitch, without resonance, without intensity.

A voice from which all sense of music has departed. There is no longer anything in it that rings or resonates, nothing that rises or resounds. All of the richness of sonic matter seems to have dissolved, or to have been diluted, as if it were possible to say something without a voice, and to have a voice that says nothing, a voice absolutely neutralized, struck down. That is what death is: he can't find the secret of his voice. He no longer finds in it any music, anything that might sing.

Jérôme does however try, reaching to find again the contours of his voice. But there is something that opens and closes his sentences and *which does not come from him*. It is not only that his voice seems to bend under the effort of speaking, but that it is gripped by a glacial tone, a silent sonority. François… Bahia… Canary Islands… La Graciosa… All of these shimmering words that brought to mind an enchanted island, the gaze of a child or a friend's smile, will from now on evoke nothing but the vast and somber territory of death. Each word has a strangely pale halo, like a candle, and seems now to refer only to itself, like a cylinder in the void. Sentences fade into one another and no longer make sense: all turn around a blind spot, they have left for a hostile, cold, nameless place.

That's what that blank voice is: the reality of death, its intolerable splendor. It speaks a very clear language; its articulations are precise and its message unequivocal. But it is like a voice that would come from behind a door and that door is now closed. As if all that the voice could possibly suggest—the scale of inspiration, the proliferation of inflexions, the varieties of intonation, the whole multiplicity of breathing sounds and the diversity of tones—all of it had been suddenly sucked into a creel, as if the voice itself had been entrapped by sound. In the cinema, they call *blank scenes* those where "the camera seems caught in an extreme emotion that affects the film itself." Thus, nothing exists any more except the blankness.

That is it—the blank voice you need to have heard at least once to understand it. Blank blankness, no longer any use for communicating, it ceases to perform in any way. The blank voice no longer has anything to prove, no opinion to defend, no more judgment to bring to bear: it does not even claim the right to complain or protest; it is reduced to announcements, observations. It is a voice that belongs to everyone and no one, where sounds meet without really meaning anything, where death itself echoes and reverberates, distant and steady. Gone are the thousand little muffled, hushed sounds under the tongue, those musical modulations born in the roof of the mouth and that come at every moment to bump against the line of the bottom lip, the wall of teeth, giving each voice its own particular character. The blank voice exists now only in relation to its own insignificance: the more it suffers, the more it is toneless, the more it would like to cry out and the more it dies away.

They say that our greatest pains are silent, or that suffering leaves us voiceless. That is not quite right. When a friend dies, a part of our voice dies forever with them. What we are left with is a voice deprived of its speech, of all speech, but which must all the same continue to speak, grappling with the unnamable—I can't go on. I'll go on—a voice like this pale dawn now rising over Tokyo, the color of lilac and marble, sea foam and winter, cold and wind, the color of friendships carried away by time. Blank, white like the wax of a candle, white like a squeezed wrist, like the face of the drowned man, white like a hospital bed, white like the mask and the gloves. Blank like blank verses, those that do not rhyme, are out of tune, that worm their way beneath the ground, gnawing at the dead man's flesh. Blank, white like the feather, the snow and the pearl, like the blank page on which I must now write these words. Only the fury of ink can extinguish or quell all this blank whiteness, can send it far away or undo it, distill or sublimate it.

In Japan, white was long the color of mourning. At the moment of death, the temple was closed and covered over with a large white paper to drive away evil spirits. A little table covered in flowers and incense was set up near to the death bed. The cadaver was covered with a white kimono, given a pair of sandals and some small coins for crossing the river of the Three Roads, its head turned toward the north or to the west. A cremation the color of rice or sugar, bread or salt. Up until the 16th century, the queens of France also wore white in mourning and were given the beautiful title of "white queens." Why white? Because it is the color of the shroud, of bones, of the skull, the cadaver? Not at all: because white light is the most beautiful, and one should remain dignified and *beautiful* in mourning so that on the white stone of the page, the love for the lost one which, within ourselves, keeps him alive, could then be expressed.

FADE FROM BLACK

Slowly, the whiteness of the page becomes a barely perceptible image: the white particles are like waves on a white background. It is something like an empty apartment, a snowy background or a slab of marble. The light is at once beautiful and unsettling, almost unreal.

The beginning of a piece of music played on a harpsichord: the Goldberg Variations*—two keyboards, treasure troves of inventiveness, frequent crossing of the hands. It is the 25th variation, the one Wanda Landowska named "The Black Pearl." The text emerges, while on the trembling surface black letters appear, fading in and out.*

The first title appears, centered, at the same time as a vertical black line spreads on the left of the screen, from top to bottom:

FRANÇOIS

The camera descends and slides along the line. Its slow movement accompanies and accentuates the music's rhythm. The 25th variation is one of the few for which Bach left directions for tempo on his personal copy, discovered in Strasbourg in 1974 and written by his own hand: adagio. That is to say, calmly, moderately, while walking slowly... The rest of the title appears exactly at the moment when the left vertical line touches the edge of the frame:

PORTRAIT D'UN ABSENT

Now, the camera steadies itself. A fixed long shot on ground level. The sound of a bird's wings to the right, like a paper rustling. A black bird has just taken flight in the middle of a thick fog, above a road covered in snow, barely discernible. The bird is the only focal point in the sparkling purity of the shot.

While the bird disappears into the fog, you can see the shape of a car, arriving directly in the distance, its headlights on. Little by little a scene takes shape: there is the wall of a cemetery, a gate in black wrought iron and a long driveway lined with poplar trees, strong and straight (their tops stretching toward the sky, slender like a pen). The car disappears for a moment into a dip in the road. You can see now, at the foot of the trees, the shape of a homeless man sitting on the ground, close to the wall, smoking. The car reappears, closer now and coming out of the dip in the road, facing the camera. The music becomes increasingly audible.

A long shot of the snow-covered road. The whiteness of the ground now takes up only one third of the image and contrasts with the darkness of the other two thirds, where all the signs of a driveway leading to the entrance of a cemetery gradually come into focus.

The sound of slamming car doors.

A silhouette comes out of the whiteness and walks toward the camera. Then another. They move forward while looking at the sky. They peer into the sky as if they are looking for answers or to enter into communion with the dead. A low-angle shot of the dark sky and the swirling snowflakes. Thanks to the music, the snow evokes less a sense of coldness than a certain lightness settling onto everything.

With a last flap of its wings, the bird finally leaves the frame to the right. The title disappears suddenly, as do all the other captions, then the vertical line fades from top to bottom.

*

It is in the Montmartre Cemetery where François lies buried, dead at the age of forty-seven. I had first got to know him thirty years earlier in Paris, when we were students. Together, we had dreamed of making a fictional film about love and quantum physics, and it now turns out to be a book that I must write in his absence.

A snowy day. I have entered the cemetery by the main gates. It is winter. Though I do not know exactly where the grave is, Sylvia told me that it is in the northwestern section, so I head vaguely in that direction: I go ahead, walking on the white pathway. A very soft and very pale sun throws some faint golden light on the gravestones, bringing a shine to the rusty joints on the railings, the ornamental hinges on the vaults. The sun is a blessing: wherever it lands, even on a grave, it brings that soft dazzle to the eye, which makes the grave seem to be moving, imparting for an instant the effervescence of crystal to the monotony of stone and bronze.

This black stone, rough and singed by time, is also softened by the presence of the snow, which has fallen over Paris all through the night. Under the blue sky, a gentle but cold breeze shakes the bunches of flowers, speckled in white. The silhouettes of the trees are reflected clear and pure on the blue-shaded snow: chestnut trees, maples, lime trees, thujas... shadows of trees as light as human souls. All around are the black graves, leaning against the impalpable darkness.

I came in by the main entrance because the Joseph de Maistre entry on the other side is open only on All Saints' Day. It is one of the many oddities that make this cemetery so interesting: despite being one of the three biggest graveyards in the city, you can enter it only from the Avenue Rachel. The "Avenue" Rachel is in fact a simple street: it has neither the breadth nor the majesty of the other avenues in the City of Lights. Its out of the way location, two steps from the busy Place de Clichy, its incongruous and in many ways paradoxical situation—it is at once a dead-end and an access road—lend to it so to speak the role of a sieve between the hustle and bustle of the surrounding main roads (Boulevard de Clichy, Rue Blanche, Boulevard des Batignolles…) and the silence of the graveyard. Except for the people who live there, or who visit the residents, the vast majority of those who take the Avenue Rachel do so to get to the Montmartre Cemetery. One might even say that this street—which is actually quite short but is lined with large trees that give it the look of a bat with plant-like skin—is the entrance to the kingdom of the dead.

As soon as you ask questions of them, the streets talk, they tell stories. Beneath its discreet appearance, Avenue Rachel has a quite unusual history: under the Occupation, it was one of the streets that Paul Sézille, the director of the Institute for the Study of Jewish Questions, wished to mark with a yellow star... In effect, as the name suggests, Rachel was of Jewish origin. That admirable tragedienne, who in the space of a few years went from begging on the streets to the Théâtre Français, and who was to revivify on stage the plays of Corneille, Racine, and Voltaire, always suffered from anti-Semitism, in life as in death: "the eldest daughter of Homer and Sophocles," as a theatre critic labeled her, had the misfortune of having the same name as

Jacob's cousin. In the France of the time, perhaps no more than in our own time, this was not a trivial detail. I wonder what François would have made of this story. He would have found it absurd, no doubt—but no more so than marking a yellow star onto a jacket, a shirt, an apron. He was on the lookout for these multiple, invisible, left out or forgotten events that made up the flipside—but were the very *lifeblood*—of contemporary history.

A gust of whiteness blows a little group of disheveled walkers into the cemetery. They trample and wade through the mud… Farther away, you hear the joyful shouts of children playing. They have red noses, red cheeks, red hands under their woolen scarves. Children love snow, as snow covers things up: they search, they find, they laugh, and their breath rises like steam from a teapot.

I advance. I observe. I am also searching. We often think of cemeteries as peaceful, luminous places, where the dead person's loved ones are invited to recall their happiest memories… But for me, I am above all interested in the decorated plaques, the ornamental or artistic scenes (mythological engravings, religious mottos, ironic epigrams), the close interlacing of flowers and letters on the steles. I enter into cemeteries as I enter into countries: via flowers and writing, landscapes and language, via history. It is a funereal region, implanted with graves: each one has its own traits, its *character*. More than anything, the inscriptions catch my attention, like a story that is dreamy and precise at once, made up only of proper names and a few phrases, as beautiful as they are unpredictable: the patterns of Roman letters, of Hebrew graphemes, of Chinese ideograms, their assertive, horizontal, vertical and sometimes even oblique power, their silent insolence, the explosive depth hidden beneath their ingenious downstrokes. These figures and these terms—all the scriptural splendor of cemeteries—seem to me not so much the vestiges of life but its irreducible affirmation.

I advance. Leaves and flowers lie trapped in ice. I go in search of François. He is here somewhere with his daughter, hidden away behind an ironwood tree and a witch hazel plant. I pass under the Caulaincourt bridge... Another anomaly: with its iron pillars straddling the cemetery, the bridge shaves the tops of the funerary monuments. Some of the dead are thus buried twice: they lie beneath the stone slabs and the pillars of the bridge. The devotees of Stendhal took years to remove him from beneath this iron framework, he who loved nothing better than the sun.

Next, I pass before Fragonard, or rather, before his ghost. The author of *Le Verrou*, who also decorated the most sumptuous apartments of Paris, does not even have a tomb to himself as it was taken away by the upheavals of successive cemetery reconfigurations. A simple plaque on the edges, by the central roundabout, recalls that he was "buried in the cemetery." I think of Isidore Ducasse, buried not far from here in the northern section, and whose grave has never been found. I have a soft spot for these will o' the wisps: even in death do they remain free spirits.

Northwest, farther still to the northwest. I advance through the ice, I search for the passage. It is a maze, looking for a dead friend: all paths open up and close over in twists and turns... I navigate between the tombs. On leaving the main pathways, there are gullies and passes, inlets and straits. I do not find François' tomb. The wind has strengthened now, it is harsher, more violent. The sun has disappeared, eaten up by the dark clouds. I skate, I slide, I advance, my gaze fixed on the tops of the crosses. It is not here... nor there... The snow hits me straight in the face, makes me close my eyes. Here I am, surrounded by graves and ice.

In the distance, I hear a song coming out of a neighboring building, carried by the wind: a radio sitting on a window ledge.

The wind shakes the mound, rushes in, engulfs the graves… What has become of my friends, those whom I have held so close, loved so much… They have become too scarce, I believe, I think the wind took them away. Under the biting wind, all leaves fall.

Glacial silence. The cemetery is now completely deserted. The shouts of the children have all faded. I have to face up to it: I will not find it today, the grave. It is late, it is too cold, I need to leave. I map out the route that will lead me back to Avenue Rachel and, through the narrow pathways that frame the graves, I end up back on the paved road. As I leave the cemetery I pass by him again. The homeless man. I watch him from a distance. He walks away in his threadbare coat. He too is cut through by the cold. He walks very slowly along the sidewalk and, at the point where he is about to cross the Rue Blanche, he almost loses his balance, shoved in the back by a gust of wind and a handful of dead leaves.

*

I return home. The little studio apartment on the Rue d'Orchampt, facing the square, with the desk next to the window and the terrace overlooking the trees. It is here that I live when I am in Paris.

I turn on the computer. The little rectangle of light appears. The Internet, the world's attic: we drown ourselves there as in an abyss or we dive into it as into a chest. Some lock themselves in there, others get lost, others still die of boredom. The Internet is a jungle. I sometimes spend all night exploring it. But this evening, a window opens right away, burning itself onto my eyes:

Tags: Death, Radio
6th January 2014
Death of François Christophe

The world of radio is in mourning. There is an homage by Yves Nilly, senior vice-president of the SACD, the Union of Authors and Playwrights.

François Christophe died accidentally, along with his daughter Bahia, during their end of year celebrations. François Christophe worked with authors and actors on creative projects. He was one of the "new breed" of drama directors at Radio France. Forty-seven years old, graduate of the FEMIS film and television school, hugely talented, intellectually curious, endearing, with a wonderful personality, which is what everyone said after working with him or merely having met him. In the space of a few years, he had breathed new life into radio drama. That is his legacy.

His latest productions, serializations of *Millennium* and *Les Misérables*, are impressive. With his background in cinema, he had a natural inclination for "radio movies," but he liked above all to work with the evocative power of radio to bring people together, mixing them up as he mixed genres, with a rare sensitivity and respect for the listening public. Whether it was dramatic series, poetry with Jean-Pierre Siméon, or "Black Nights" on France Inter, he always gave his work the same energy and attention.

This news has affected many of us greatly. Our thoughts are with his wife and his family.

I do not know Yves Nilly, but he sums things up well. Highly talented, curious, likeable... Energy and attention to detail... Yes, that is François: a beautiful person. An accurate portrait.

And yet, something is missing: the darker side of François, his radical intensity and, at the same time, intrinsically connected to the latter, the poetic side that would completely overtake him, that strong, deep side he had... People don't know: it's a whole unknown territory they will be deprived of. He had things he still wanted to do... not only radio shows that pierced the air and crossed space to bombard the listeners of France Culture with emotions, but perhaps also films, the documentaries that he was so good at making. He was a mine, a treasure chest. Here lies François, a sediment deposited into the earth.

You would have to extend, unfold, and open out all the potential he had in him. At heart, everyone is like one of those scrolls that, since the invention of paper in 1st Century China, spread across the Far East and that François loved so much: *Eight Flowers* by Qian Xuan, the *Illustrated Biography of the Monk Ippen*, the *Illustrated Sutra of Cause and Effect*… A blue river of ink, sketches brocaded with gold and silver, a burst of ideograms: that would be François' scroll. You would have to take your time, lay it out on a mat, then patiently unroll it, section by section, as if you were beginning a journey, as if you were walking in a landscape painting. Then, the *real movie* of his life could open out and spread across this screen of paper, with its shadowy zones and its savage light, between a jade-green border and a wooden stick, on a backing woven in silk.

*

In mourning, the world turns in the opposite direction. The rotation of the Earth slows down and its axis changes, it seems to turn around in space and tilt onto another plane altogether. The distribution of mass changes, there is a redistribution of pain, joy, anger, of the continents we carry within ourselves. The change in direction brought about by death affects all of our thoughts, from the most trivial to the most important, from the most precious to the most meaningless; mourning takes hold very quickly and all reading processes are shaken up by it.

It is my turn now to feel gripped by absence. Especially in the evening, when the day's light fades and then dies, despondency engulfs me. I am short of breath, I am caught by the "mournful silent stupidity which doth pierce us so when accidents surpassing our strength overwhelm us" that Montaigne writes of. Montaigne knew what it was to lose a friend: he never really recovered from that loss, and in a way his entire oeuvre came out of it. Now I am in my bed, and he is in his. We are separated forever and can never again be of one mind. My tongue grows numb, a dark, icy liquid courses through my limbs, my ears hum. A double darkness covers my eyes.

*

Night has fallen. After all the whiteness at the cemetery not so long ago, night comes, and with it, blackness. I go to the window, I look outside. Snow is everywhere. The return of the severe cold.

It is a gruesome night; storms are brewing. The wind attacks now, penetrating the timbers, passing through the smallest openings, between the tired joints and the uprights. It has come to bite at and confront all that is sealed up: window frames, casings, glazing beads… The wind is just like mourning, it slips in everywhere and rattles even the sturdiest windows.

There is a point in the night when everything comes to a halt: plans, certainties, the night itself. At that point, words arrive on the scene. They come like a fever: a thousand invisible phrases explode in the shadows. A whole flotilla of terms, an armada… they have come to cruise inside me from the darkest parts of my consciousness. In the blind alleys of sleep, they rush toward me; in groups and clusters, they gather closely around me, a tumultuous rabble, lexicons and locutions, words and clauses. On the edge of silence, you can hear their soft whisperings. I must listen, must descend even lower, deeper, pass to the other side, mining in a minor key. I must melt away, become a shadow, make myself worthy of their darkness.

I see a slight tear on the sheet, and it is as if the whole bedroom is about to disappear down this little hole. I suddenly find myself in the presence of certain details of my life, but which appear reflected by an indented mirror and catapult themselves to the four corners of the room. Fragments of phrases break away and images appear. Balusters, ornamental lakes… Cypress trees, flowery tablecloths… It is Versailles. We are walking, François and I, we are looking for the statue of Louis XIV sculpted by Bernini but are unable to find it. I remember this walk, but in the half-sleep that is taking me over, the scene is strangely chiseled, like the cold and distant light of a sunray on a broken cup.

It is Versailles, but it is not Versailles. A vague burning smell floats across the lakes, in the air glints of flames pass by. There are trunks of black trees sticking out of the water, patches of snow on the bank, spots of gray soot. "We must find Versailles again!" François tells me, his voice trembling. We walk on, the statue is on the island, they have locked it away in a dungeon. It is a trap, I can sense it, an open trap in the crimson shadows… On the ground large shapeless shadows stretch out like pieces of laundry blown by the wind.

We are entering a large derelict building and François suddenly disappears. I try to get back to him, I bump into pieces of furniture, worm-eaten tables, I push open a door, climb a flight of stairs, and here, in the middle of what I thought was total darkness, I find myself before a green, translucent bay window, the green of an oak tree or of algae, the green of an insect. Then I hear a humming sound, the cogs of the mechanism become disconnected, turn backwards, then reconnect. I understand everything: the architect has forgotten to build the child's bedroom. There is a dead center in the castle and the staircase leads to a dead end. Whichever path you take, you always end up there. The sound of loud footsteps on the staircase. My heart beats like a drum.

"François!" I call his name in the darkness. But there is always a price to pay for calling out the names of the dead. The trap is now deployed from all sides of the darkness. I see François coming back, he has passed by the bay window, his head stretches out like a dog's muzzle. The crypt is walled and he has not found the statue: it must have run away in the night, mounted on its hurricane horse. Now all of his limbs are covered in white powder, under a black overcoat. His body looks like that of a Butoh dancer, as if he is set in talcum, but his face remains in the shadows, he is literally eaten up by the shadows. He is terribly pale, a cone of darkness on his face.

He is a large deathly form. It looks like him, but at the same time I do not recognize him. Has he come to look for me? Or is it I who must take him somewhere? I have forgotten or I no longer know, but I should know. He comes to remind me of our very old alliance. François… He knows things about me, I know things about him. We are the only ones who know. That is what friendship is, this shared knowledge, the others don't know, it is the knowledge of the matters of death. And who will be my redeemer? A man with a bull's head? Or a bull with a man's head? One day, a wave will also carry me away and I will go to join him. At that point I will become forever incomprehensible to others, impenetrable to others. I will enter into the exclusion zone and, this time, will not return.

It is now the end: we are on a foreign island in the middle of a triangular forest devoured by the tides. The sun is setting: incandescent in the sunset, the island drills its stempost into the sea. François is with Bahia, he runs and takes her in his arms, the wave suddenly passes over him, submerges him, and kills him with her, the two of them coiled up together… All that remains at the end are a pushed-back face and a hand fallen to the ground like a pebble.

I see him! He is there! He is there again, alone on the bank. I throw myself toward him, but he is no longer there. This time I know for sure: François is dead.

*

François is dead, François is dead, the phrase keeps coming back to me, as if it were at once a question and its only response. In the morning, after getting up, making the coffee… In the afternoon, doing the shopping, at the supermarket… This single phrase, all throughout the day. And every time I think I have finished with it, the phrase comes buzzing back like a fly in the mouth, a bee at your ears, and I have to say it again, as that is all it demands: to be said, to be resaid.

Someone has died. A crazy procession of speech gone mad, that no longer knows exactly what it must say or how to say it, which no longer knows anything other than repeating the same words for days and months at a time.

*

Last night's nightmares—almost hallucinations—have left me drained. With this exhausting mourning at all-out war with me in the wintertime… It is as if death had visited me in person, as if it had come to ask for my response.

Death at first dazzles, it bewilders—then it blinds, it walls itself in, it crashes. Tomb, death, mourning, how heavy these words are… A gloomy sound of rumination takes hold of the narration of the days. You have to get out of there, the dark depths of the mind. Since François died, I go often to the window, drawn irresistibly to the rotunda that overlooks the square. From here, I can see the back façade of the Bateau-Lavoir and it is here that the *Demoiselles d'Avignon* were revealed for the first time, more than a century ago now, in a little brick and wood house built on the side of a collapsed quarry.

The history of the Bateau-Lavoir should be better known: a dozen artists' workshops with a single water point close to which laundry was laid out to dry, which gave the building its name. A few poorly heated studios, but with great windows through which the light rushes in: undulations, radiance, vibrations, it was the "central laboratory for modern painting," as Max Jacob said. When the old building fell down following the collapse of a quarry, it was first replaced by an open-air dance hall, then by this set of workshops. What? New beginnings might come out of emptiness, silence, and shadows? That is how in any case modern art was born on the site of an old piano factory and a popular dance hall: thanks to a landslide.

There are many sketches of Picasso's *Demoiselles* found in ill-assorted, explosive notebooks that show the multiple paths he took toward the final version: sketches in black pencil or in graphite, studies of faces or chests, portraits with the eyes looking downward... Shoulder blades, collarbones, eyebrows, large nude bodies leaning backward or with the arms reaching out in front: the human body from every angle. In his attic, Picasso knew better than anyone else how to transform the deadweight of memory into a living burst of faces and gestures. As in all art, it was simply a matter of *making something appear*.

François, Bahia... They are dead. This truth has to be spoken. Nothing ever replaces someone who has gone. No compensation, not even any consolation: the funeral road never leads to a reunion. In truth, it leads to nothing.

Soon, it will be too late. Silence will cover over everything like the snow. All that will remain then will be this book, like a force that has been captured somewhere, one day, and that as soon as it is opened and its pages are turned finds itself by a miracle put back into circulation somewhere else.

I turn around, I go toward my library. It is my turn to play now. Literature is the art of mourning par excellence and, in its very fragility, paper is superior to marble. And yet, what dark work it is to pull this thing out, this book... It is a tomb, it needs to be made as serious as marble and as light as the sky.

Now their bodies are lost and the old miser of ice and frost holds their souls captive in his leather purse. The real tomb is that of forgetting and so I am writing this book to fight against that second death that is to be forgotten. I am not really going to speak of their death, but rather of my relation to these deaths, this strange and fragile attachment that, through the days, months, and years, connects and reconnects us—until the time comes of our own, always unimaginable, death—to those we love and who leave us.

PART ONE: THE 400 BLOWS

1. THE LYCÉE LAKANAL

The images come one after the other, as in a film. Sometimes, the film derails and ends up stuck on one of the images. It is at this precise moment that writing comes into play. It is not the image that I am looking for, but the persistent effect of a presence. Thus, the text does not provide the frame for a memory, but the opening up of a space: it is a sort of breach where time circulates, where memory reawakes, leaps into life.

Now, sentences take flight and rise to take the little bedroom by storm, hidden in the heart of the triangle formed by the Avenue du Président-Franklin-Roosevelt, the Avenue Claude-Perrault, and the Allée-d'Honneur leading straight to the Château de Sceaux. They cross over the railings, rush into the courtyard, dash to the preparatory class building, climb up the southwestern wing, edge their way into the corners, cross days and nights.

Words have no final place, they exist only in their leaping movement, in their relationships with other words and other texts, in the space they open up or that they fill between the past centuries and the books to come... They set out to encounter a lively eye, a well-tuned ear, a sharp tongue, which could give back to them the joy of new breath: what we call a soul.

Sentences, sentences, are the noise of the blood which circulates joyously, before the sea drinks them, before death takes them, before silence crushes them.

*

Arriving in front of number 3 Avenue du Président-Franklin-Roosevelt in Sceaux, you stop for a minute. Are you really standing in front of a scholarly establishment? Supported by two stone walls, the great sea-green gate is surrounded by a grill made of wrought iron and above it there is a frieze of metallic branches: a series of interlaced stems fans out in a succession of indentations, lobes, and serrations. Like arrows shot from a quiver, festoons reach into the higher parts and the corners, sliding across the stone walls, grafting themselves onto the gray tiles on the roofs. There is nothing flashy here, no frills: the pure contours of the original, century-old design unwind in moldings and spirals.

The door opens onto a vast park that is reached by way of a steep, paved pathway. There is a cedar tree on the left, an oak on the right. Thus, between the emblem of eastern splendor and the symbol of the northern hemisphere, you enter into the Lycée Lakanal as if you were edging your way to the heart of all worlds. Farther down, a pine tree from Corsica, a tulip tree from Virginia, a prune tree from Iran, a giant sequoia from California. A great silence, growing and growing the closer you get to the main building, imposes itself: the sounds of the street die out, you could hear a flea walking, a frog sliding, a butterfly flying.

Then, everything is open, shaded, arithmetical: the farther you go the more you marvel at the quietude of the place and the size of the park. The woods are deep and the path rises steeply. A grand sense of solitude. The September mists whiten the black branches of the chestnut trees, the frost shudders and cracks underfoot. Along the hazel trees that line the paths, butterflies pass by like winged flowers. All around, superimposed layers of tree branches reach skyward. The branches and leaves make you think of the entry gate: the secret of the universe has been pierced, trees and geometry complement each other, a set of undulations crosses the tops of the buildings which stand out in the distance against the changing taffetas of the foliage.

A faint scent of resin floats over everything, a smell flavored softly with camphor, tender and calming. It is a yellow, grainy, crisp smell, the perfume of the witches of the woods. In the distance, near to a cherry tree from Japan that marks the entrance to the classrooms, you can see some silhouettes wrapped up in big cotton or linen coats. That is them, the *Scéennes*, the high-school girls, the young queens of Sceaux, of its high school and its castle, of its park and its gardens. They pass, slender, haughty and upright between the oaks and the hornbeams, like stems of white lilac. Love hangs in the air under the cherry trees.

Animals discreetly populate this park and its surrounding areas. The song of the robin accompanies the visitor as he crosses the park to climb toward the buildings. The fluted trunk of the myrtle tree, the willow with its twisted branches, let loose flights of thrushes, flocks of sparrows. A look sideways to the undergrowth reveals bunches of tree frogs and grass snakes in corners covered with wild shrubs and Virginia creepers. Farther away, there is a whole flower bed of squirrels chewing on seeds, nibbling on berries.

Finally, as the slope becomes less steep, you come progressively to a series of four square courtyards, planted with trees at regular intervals and scattered with brown chestnut tree leaves. The buildings are multicolored: brick, clay, and metal form its framework while multitudes of red, ochre and orangey strokes stuck into the whiteness of the stonework contrast with the gray flecks of the turrets. These blobs of bright color form little banners of golden light all over the walls, impalpable like glimmers and shimmering like stained glass.

Lakanal… at the very mention of this name the powers arise… It is a city within the city, a town within the town, a State within one's state of mind. A strange secular monastery, at once castle and abbey, garden and library, convent and kingdom. In the sweet scent of chestnut, sheltered by the trees and their benevolent influence, your senses open out and children as much as adults develop there a singular power of perception. For Lakanal is not a high school: it is an island. A strange exception, a condensed version of Frenchness, between the ironwork and the tapestry, the precious stone and the arabesque, the honeycomb and the crown. Lakanal has a poetic density. This poetry is linked directly to the site. The light, the sound, the lines, the colors, the mosses, the wind, the birds... these are Lakanal's weapons.

It was at the Lycée Lakanal, having just turned seventeen, that I first met François.

2. FRANÇOIS AT HIS WINDOW

I remember the first time I saw François at the Lycée Lakanal. He is in the bedroom next to mine, right in the middle of the corridor, at its heart, so to speak, or better still, its epicenter. Quite by chance, over the following two years, our rooms would be next door to each other, successively on the second and third floors. We were neighbors from the beginning, and I will feel close to him for all my life.

Suddenly, an abrupt sense of clarity, a beautiful, frosty Thursday evening, there is François. I am arriving with my suitcase. He is standing alone in the middle of the corridor. Who is he? What is he doing here? I do not know him. And yet it seems like I do know him. And even, standing there like that in the middle of the corridor, it seems to me like he is waiting for me.

François is above all a "funny-looking guy," a *Drôle de corps* as in the title of a piece by Couperin, a musician he loved so much. Nature has given him an elongated look: his nose is well defined, his shoulders thin and slouched, his head slightly rounded at the top and at the lower part of his chin. Nothing goes sideways with him, everything points upwards very quickly (his thick eyebrows, that he raises often to the sky) or slides to the bottom very slowly (his thin mouth, which sighs softly). His hair is also long, back then almost touching his shoulders. Light brown and shiny, extremely soft to touch. He is quite well groomed, more like a sack of wheat than a hay bale, but there are always a few rebellious locks that stick out at the sides.

He does not have a shapely body. There is nothing big or overly impressive about his physique. His stomach is flat, almost thin, his arms are long: he is not at all muscular, but a rickety structure, like a house that is about to collapse. And yet as a whole, he gives off a great impression of vigor and energy, a bit like those slender boxers who don't seem to be well equipped physically, but who strike quickly and at all angles, to the stomach, the sides, the face, in repeated patterns that finally succeed in unsettling heavyweights with a more rigid style and stockier, less mobile combatants. Being long-limbed and rangy, such were his strengths, paradoxical and contradictory. He is lanky, long and slender: like a pencil, an outline sketched by a quill, a figure drawn by a reed.

Although nearly six feet tall, François stoops, dressed in big woolen sweaters or large white cotton shirts that always make him seem to be floating as he moves. He comes into your room without ever knocking, without warning, without announcing himself: he walks in, preceded by his arms and hands like the octopus and its tentacles, elegant and gangly, unfurling and proliferating, spindly and slender. It is impoliteness itself, but he is so charming and his conversation is so thrilling that his visits are always welcome.

François is an octopus: his arms are too long and his hands too big, yet they are the lovely slim hands of a pianist, with manicured fingernails and slender fingers that seem always to need to devour the space around them. When he speaks, he seems to have eight arms, sixteen hands, thirty-two fingers, sixty-four phalanxes, and thousands of nerve endings... If you give him a keyboard, the whole room fills with his passion—Bach, Couperin, Handel, and then Scarlatti or Bach again: in a few moments the space rises up, grows larger, amplifies, takes on new, lofty shapes and is transformed into a cathedral of sounds. If you give him a text to read or comment on—Rimbaud, for example, whom he venerates, or Saint-Simon, on whom he would write his Master's thesis—his hands suddenly stop moving, become calm, his mouth opens to a great silence, everyone literally drinks in his commentaries: his explanations are passionate but dry, clear and precise, without any snobbery or jargon at all. With him, dryness replaces coarseness, density surpasses mass. He is a sharp body, all lines and movements, a hyperacute presence.

How is a friendship born? No one knows. But between us there is from the beginning something urgent and alive. It has nothing to do with rational thinking, the mind, or calculation. It is not founded on any reasoning, but on an intuitive experience—physical and intellectual at the same time—of this very particular presence.

*

There are parts of the body that are never spoken about, but that say much about a human being, their weaknesses or strengths, their secrets. Absent parts, blank spots. In most cases, we claim to understand people by asking them about their past or their plans, by making them speak of their (supposed) failures or their (claimed) successes. It is the mire of bad psychology, that which claims to explain everything based on a selection of the following: the mystery of families, the network of social relations, or the swarm of romantic liaisons, all of which are most often inextricably linked in an appalling confusion. But you can't shake off the body in that way. Often, the precise movement of the shoulders or the line of a mouth teaches you more than the always uncertain explanation of a series of volatile intentions.

*

Memory is first a question of physiology and then a psychological phenomenon. The legs, the arms are full of numbed recollections. Begin with the skin, the complexion, observe the figure, the bearing. Then look at the color of the face, note the bags under the eyes, scrutinize the lines on the forehead. Listen closely to the voice, the breathing, but also the beating of the heart, the regrets that may be read like graffiti on the sides of the temples, the hopes that persist for a long time in the shivering of the lungs. The unique key of psychology thus gives way to a bunch of perceptions that permit at times a glimpse of the twinkling of the minuscule precious stones that every person accumulates in the deepest part of their being.

All these parts of the body are at once the most difficult to reach and the most essential. We lack a certain number of organs to do this, but wherever sight or smell abandon us, there is a certain internal sense – personal, private, and deep – an interior scalpel that writing allows us to sharpen, a mysterious string that it alone knows how to make vibrate.

With François, for example, everything goes through the eyebrows. He can raise, lower, or wrinkle his brow in a thousand ways, ever revealing the astonishing range of thoughts and emotions that course though him at full speed and at all times. As in the Nô theatre, where a slow and barely delineated gesture, but with calculated range and quite specific orientation, can indicate in turn a distant mist-covered mountain, a sunrise, or the song of a bird, the slightest inflection of his eyebrows suggests a different mood or thought. When an uninvited guest comes to disturb him while he is listening to music, he frowns in a worried way, as if he has just been elbowed in the stomach, but once the visitor has left, I see the skyline of his eyebrows settle back peacefully into their previous shape. When he evokes the splendors of Rome or Venice, the line of his eyebrows traces the shape of an archway. When he speaks of the shorelines of Senegal battered by the Atlantic winds and of the whirlwinds that sweep the north of the country, they get all bushy and battered: each eyebrow becomes a headland torn and beaten by the stormy sea.

Finally, when he watches *The Gospel According to Saint Matthew* by Pasolini, his right eyebrow leans to the right as if he were holding a monocle there. This simple inflection transforms his pupil into a disc that cuts like a diamond and gives him a look of dark intensity: you really sense that he is absorbing the film, being inhabited by it, analyzing all of its elements, the production, the framing, the movements of the camera… Yet this remarkable internal rumination is visible only at the peak of his eyebrow.

*

There is also his beard. François always wears a three-day beard. Not two, nor four, no: three days, not one day, more or less. It is according to him the right balance between the fuzz of the beginnings of a beard, the *prima barba*, or the "wispy beard" as they called it in the 18th century, and the bushy growth of older beards.

François likes neither the nonchalant-style beard nor one that looks too affected. He wants neither a sharp, overly meticulous, little beard nor a big, unkempt bushy one. He dislikes overworked and high maintenance beards as much as carefree and lazy beards: he wants a beard like the one the ivy gives to the statues in the Parc de Sceaux, moving, subtle, light, almost indeterminate, of a deep black and a very precise contour.

He would have been annoyed by—would have bristled at—the new beards you see everywhere these days, the trendy beards of the hipsters, squared off and thick in such a way that from a distance you might easily take them for bears, but all standardized into an identical model with very little variation, nuances, or tones. Or those, now almost obligatory, of politicians wanting to become members of the government: cynical beards, partisan beards, sprouting over a few nights on the chins of the careerists that give them the air of the second in command at their offices. A thick yet well-disciplined beard befits the seriousness of this new clergy, at once an attribute of power and a new sign of respectability. That's not even to mention the beards of the fanatics, that are the flip side of their lack of virility, their basic impotence. To hell with all these beards! Wearing a beard in a dignified way seems to have become almost unthinkable today.

François is very careful with his own: he grows his three-day beard with particular care. It is as he says himself: he is very carefully unshaven.

*

The more I observe him the more François seems to me to be far more saturnine than the gentle and cheerful image that he gives off at first sight. His eyes are green and cheery. His mouth always has the starry look of a very faint smile. But if you look at him more closely you can see an abyss palpitating beneath his eyelids, a crack that seeps into the thin smile floating on his lips. This velvety-skinned face has sites of shade and torment: still young, it is already creased with little wrinkles and marked by dark circles which reveal his penchant for parties and late nights but are also traces of worry and even of anxiety. To study him more attentively, every physical detail seems to be marked by agitation, sometimes disorder, sometimes doubt: François is a very complex being.

His chest is rarely upright: François is not only long and stooped, he is often leaning over. When he listens to music, when he looks at a painting, when he explains something... If the word *character* designates at once a way of thinking and a printer's letter, then François is an *i*, in italics. Something pulls him to the abyss while simultaneously hoisting him to the heights.

Certain aspects of his physical appearance are delicate, trembling, hesitant lines (his hands notably, which are always moving), while others are straighter, more slender, with more angular transitions (his lower neck, his thin, readily pinched lips), which denote his great determination. His body is at once abrupt and undulating, by turns regal and stumbling, hesitant and triumphant. You find the same complexity in his attitudes: his cruel jibes on the one hand, his tenderness and devotion on the other. He mocks everyone, but he is willing to listen to anyone. It is a strange mix of nonchalance and nervousness. He is very handsome and very contradictory.

The best example is the way he walks. It is the opposite of a regular, monotonous stride. François walks as if he is always on the move between several worlds, getting around in spattering movements or reverberations: turns and detours, curves and diversions, like a series of bounces skimming over water, whispers across space, a set of wandering movements that seem to have no goal other than to cover their tracks and to throw off any pursuit.

Around fifteen minutes into Charlotte Zwerin's magnificent portrait of Thelonious Monk, *Straight No Chaser*, you see the pianist backstage at the Five Spot Café as he strolls around in a delightful way: he stops abruptly, starts again, false starts, repeats himself... He smiles, he is serious, he has fun. It is as if he is trying to catch a butterfly. A few minutes later, he is en route for his first world tour, leaping from one concert to the next, from Geneva to Australia. While his wife Nellie is exchanging some currency in a Swiss airport, he recommences his quadrille: a little pas de deux, two petite dance steps... It is the walk of an acrobat, always on the point of his toes.

From time to time, in the middle of a concert, he stands up from his piano and turns and turns, humming to himself, chanting silently... He is the man of a thousand turns. A matador of the invisible, seeming to pivot around a very ancient minotaur. His hands thrust into the piano banderillas of unpredictable sound. While airplanes spin around the world and bankers' hands move from one bundle of cash to the next, the fingers of Thelonious Sphere Monk twirl around the piano and he throws down the shapes of his swirling rodeo at every point on the globe.

People have said that Monk was mad, that he was afflicted with a kind of autism or schizophrenia, or with a form of unidentified mental illness. Yes, that is possible. But while the bankers' dance never ends, he seems to be the only one to be properly reasonable, the only one to keep his power of improvisation and bifurcation intact in every situation.

François and I admire Monk immensely. Seeing him walking in Zwerin's film was a revelation: Monk does not walk step by step, but dances, sings and plays—he thinks and walks in the same step. His music is in close harmony with his body and his way of living. François' way of walking is not so arresting: it is less jaunty, less dashing, slower and more flowing. But it is like Monk's, not because he imitates him but because, like Monk, he is always a little off center, always a step to the side.

This gives him a slightly dapper, dashing air. It is also, as I would learn later, a mark of instability, yet at the time I saw nothing but its most alluring effects. A form of letting go, of permanent destabilization. He is never where you expect him to be, but he is not ever where you would not expect him to be, either. Always, at all times, he composes his own topography.

*

Nothing is more difficult than talking about friendship. What is friendship? No one has a clue, and the hypotheses abound on the same scale as our ignorance. Friendship is a phantom: difficulty erupts as soon as you try to define it. Today still, today especially, there are friends everywhere, and yet it is more invisible than ever. And all of the Facebook "friends" confirm more than ever what La Fontaine said long ago:

> *Everyone calls himself a friend; but it is a fool who counts on it*
> *Nothing is more common than the name,*
> *Nothing is rarer than the thing.*

We need to face facts. In the great confusion of the world, no one knows what friendship is. Even Montaigne, the great Montaigne, the master of all of us, knew not what to say of it, getting out of it however with a magnificent pirouette: "*Because he was he, because I was I.*" It is one of Montaigne's most droll phrases, just by its very drollness. By its simple formulation, it says to us:

friendship is something plainly obvious and at the same time it is elusive, it slips away from you the more you try to know it.

It is no doubt one of Montaigne's most famous sayings, one of the most read and most commented on. Though I would say that we don't really know the conditions in which it was written well enough. In the first edition of the *Essais* in fact, this phrase is much flatter, even banal: "If you press me to say why I loved him, I feel that it cannot be expressed."

It is in the *posthumous* edition of 1595, described as "based on the Bordeaux Copy," that we find the more elaborate version: "If you press me to say why I loved him, I feel that it can be expressed only by responding: *because he was he, and I was I.*" The addition of the famous short phrase was made by Montaigne's own hand, in the margins of his personal copy, as if he were coming back from beyond the grave to enlighten us.

Yet, what strikes me in this phrase is less the substance of what he says than the very movement he puts into it. Rather than admitting his powerlessness ("I feel that it cannot be expressed"), Montaigne, like an archer, fires off a magnificent line: "Because he was he; because I was I." The message in itself is disconcerting: it is an explanation that explains nothing, a bit offhand and enigmatic. But the essential element is elsewhere. This precision made in the margins is in fact a perfect alexandrine (because for a Gascon-French bilingual of the 16th century, the final **e** is pronounced). And this alexandrine can be read in every tone: it can be sung, whispered, cited or recited, chanted like a prayer or a slogan, whistled, chirped, declaimed or hummed. Knowledge is shifted, whispered, scribbled in the margins of the book, stitched into its lining: the secret is finally revealed.

What Montaigne tells us through this phrase, which is rightfully memorized by everyone, is that the knowledge of friendship is unlike any other. Friendship is a music: it is always vain—

indeed a little absurd—to try to explain it, but you can be its sharp-witted interpreter. Friendship is not a substance that you can "explain," like you extract from a body the liquid it contains, but it is elucidated only when it is split, broken down into parts, the sound of a voice in space, an arm leaning on a shoulder, the way a hand moves across paper.

Two solitudes suddenly catch sight of each other, call out, listen, respond to each other. It is more a relational than a rational experience, musical before being social. If we have such need of it, if we miss it so much when by misfortune it breaks down or is interrupted, it is that this experience is constitutive of the happiness of existence. Indeed, one could even say that it is its most obvious, immediate, and unadorned foundation.

*

François enters. He is a stream of air. As soon as he enters, the air circulates. He is a breath of oxygen. The whole room grows bigger, lighter, reorganizes itself around him.

I see François once again at the window of his bedroom in that early September, his head lifted to the pale blue sky, his gaze turned to the Parc des Sceaux. Outside, the courtyard, surrounded by the red and yellow trees of autumn. He observes the gardens embroidered by *Le Nôtre*, he listens to the sparrows brushing by on the castle's slate roofs, he inhales the woody aromas of the ash, elm and poplar trees.

His left hand remains in the shadow while the right, pressed against his knee, holds his eternal cigarette above his head. The low light coming from the right illuminates his left side and glints onto his face. He seems to transform himself into a halo of light. Clear composition: the tight space of the bedroom opens through the window onto a vast exterior space made up of trees and birds, lighting up the surfaces of beings and things.

François, always close to the window, attentive, immobile. At night, too, when he comes back he sits by the window to smoke: from my neighboring room, I hear the familiar click of the window catch when he gets up to smoke and to contemplate the stars. As far back as I can remember, he is always close to a window bar, a windowpane, a porthole, a bay window, by which he smokes, stretching out his long frame. A whole life by the window... The window allowed him at once to shed light on an interior scene and to find again a link, by turns tense and contemplative, between himself and the external world.

It may be surprising that in portraying François I am speaking almost exclusively about his body, his facial features, his physical characteristics, his physiological magnetism. What about his feelings? His background? His belongings? His friends? His family roots? His scholarly career? His political opinions? Yes of course, these things are important, but the essential thing is not found there. The psychological and moral criteria, the social conditioning, the clinical categories, the ideological references, all that is contained in and exceeded by this body that we have and that we spend our time building or destroying, protecting or exposing, creating, shaping.

Look at your friends. Interrogate their gestures, their movements, their atoms. Read their lips, flick through their skin, decode their complexion. Penetrate their face and imagine their lungs. Interest yourself in their nervous system. Listen to their pulse. Know how to make their muscles, their tendons, speak. Patiently spell out all the nuances of their health, their humor, their character. Then, maybe, you will step softly toward the great mystery.

Thus, as far as François is concerned, his aura is not linked to—or not only to—a certain personality, a single temperament.

He is generous, he is intelligent, he is a little narcissistic, he is cultured: yes, everyone knows this. But above all, like a window, he creates a certain kind of light. He flows, he circulates inside the shadows. He is a sentence in movement, sometimes dark, sometimes bright, throwing out a thousand lights and just as many nuances, illuminating some and leaving others in darkness.

When I write "François at the window," I don't want to only say that François was always attracted to windows and that he regularly leant against them from morning to evening and right through to the middle of the night. No, I write "François at the window" like "swift-footed Achilles," "grey-eyed Athena," or "Ulysses of a thousand ruses." That is to say that the window was not only a place in the room toward which François freely gravitated: he became inseparable from it. It was his Homeric epithet, the way of being in the world that he had created for himself very early on and that lasted his whole life. François was at the window like the hunter lies in wait and like the wolf is at bay.

In fact, François became the window itself. François was a window and all the windows that I now open or sit close to hold memories of François. That is what he was for me, and for each of us: radiance, a breath of oxygen and light, an opening that lets in great gusts of wind and music.

3. THE BOARDING SCHOOL

Human beings are places. They are not content with belonging to a given place, but they become that place, they transform it as you think they are adapting to it while the place itself modifies them, in deep and lasting ways, without their knowing, in a strange complementarity. We inhabit a place as much as it inhabits us.

At the time of François' and my entry into the preparatory classes of the Lycée Lakanal, Sceaux was still that peaceful haven that allowed people to escape from the nearby commotion of Paris. And the Lycée Lakanal was more than ever a splendid hive of activity in a country setting dedicated to study, an enclave of studious tranquility.

The paradox is that over two years such a peaceful place, designed for learning and dedicated to patience and knowledge, will see the blossoming of the most impetuous, the unruliest, the most turbulent "little gang" that the prestigious establishment has ever taken in. Behind the beautiful stone façades that visitors gaze at, the Lycée houses in fact a largely inconspicuous, unseen place, like a bad thought in a virtuous soul: the Boarding School.

*

Seen from the Avenue Claude-Perrault, the Boarding School appears first of all as some gigantic windows, incredibly big by today's standards, planted in the façades of the Lycée like beautiful white arches reaching up into the sky. By day, they sparkle and reflect the blinding shafts of sunlight. The stone shines like quartz and gives the whole thing the appearance of a luminous monastery that overlooks the trees and seems to speak, beyond the rows of beech and ash, to the old château de Sceaux and the gardens of *Le Nôtre* that stand just opposite, a few steps away.

But at night, the building becomes a great dark charterhouse, a library or a necropolis, its walls pierced with a few lit casement windows which look like enormous, monstrous children's heads blinking their eyes in the darkness. The walls are black and the roofs lean forward as if the building is going to collapse at any time. The boarders' bedrooms become hermits' cells dug into the flanks of the rock, suspended above inaccessible chasms. The

Boarding School is our domain, our kingdom. It crosses space and pierces time.

*

According to most of the literary production of the 19th century, the boarding school is an unhealthy place that is often compared to a barracks or a convent, indeed to a prison.

This is particularly striking with Vallès, who evokes the boarding school only in terms of darkness and squalor: "[…] it is dark, the wind blows; now and then, there are some stairs to climb, a long corridor, a darkened staircase […]." As for Balzac, in *Louis Lambert*, he describes the Collège de Vendôme as "a vast enclosure carefully closed off" under the yoke of "the classic leather ferule": the pupils there "stood in rows like soldiers," living a "life deprived of all communication with the outside," presenting "a character equally terrifying in moral and physical terms." Finally, Renan concludes his *Memories of Childhood and Youth* with the following eloquent phrase: "Boarding school drained the life from me." This says it all!

And yet. If these great authors had known the boarding school of the Lycée Lakanal, it would have changed the face of French literature! It is the complete opposite of the stuffy stereotype. The Lakanal boarding school is an admirable forge: there is always a nice surprise or some terrible stunt simmering there. It is a no-go area where the boarders are the only masters on board, where the teachers are not welcome, where the prefects are persecuted, where the day pupils never venture.

For there are the boarders and there are the day pupils, these two categories separated only by the thirty-nine steps of a stone staircase, the one that leads from the common courtyard to the upper levels, but they are enough to mark an absolute limit, a border that is almost impassable.

The day pupils, known as the *externs*, that is their name, their status, their condition—their curse!—are on the exterior. We work from the inside, we touch the living flesh, the heart, the lungs, the very core. The day pupils turn in circles and linger indefinitely in the courtyard around the same problems. We pass without stopping from one floor to the next, know the walkways and the shortcuts, experts in the art of the short circuit.

They are two ways of living, two ways of writing, two ways of feeling and being. It is unfair, but that is how it is: the day pupils will try as hard as they can, get excited by their readings, become exasperated by their studies, give their all to their essays, but they will always be outside, lagging behind, tagging along, playing chaperone. The boarders have the passkey, the magic word, the secret entry to the wild parade: they enter and leave wherever they like, when they like, they know all the glitches on the inside and all the exits leading to the outside. They are interesting, intelligent, a little full of themselves of course, but so carefree that they get away with everything.

Every morning, every evening, the day pupils come and go, wasting time in their daily routines. The boarders are onsite, on maneuvers and on the lookout, they gain time and terrain. They get up at the last minute and burst into class one by one, ruffled, ruffling! Subjected to the tedious workings of public transport, the day pupils arrive all together, slowly dragging themselves along… People think sometimes that the day pupils lead free and happy lives and that the boarders are locked up. The opposite is true: the day pupils are consigned to home, the boarders come and go as they please, in complete secrecy.

Each evening, the day pupils return home (or to some host family paid off by their own family). They have a house where they can feel at home and recharge their batteries, strongholds conquered by their fathers' money or their mothers' dowry. The boarders have only one country, one territory, that they defend proudly: the boarding school. The day pupils return to their family home, the boarders have left it for good and must carry it inside them like an immense, incandescent, independent brazier. When they go back to their families for the summer vacation, even their parents no longer recognize them: How he has grown! How he has changed! But your hair? What have you done to your hair? You're smoking now? Yes, mother, I smoke, and my hair is a mess. It no longer knows the rigors of the comb or the indignities of hair styling.

In class, it is the same thing. The day pupils pretend to have the answers but the boarders are the entomologists of the question. While the day pupils observe the texts, dissect them, analyze them, and tone them down, the boarders seize them and set them alight: they drill down into them, explore them. By comparison, the day pupils appear lackluster. They like the approved, reasoned authors while the boarders read incendiary books in secret.

Sometimes, the boarding school half opens up like the door of a chapel, to let a girl pass through or to let a boy in… The boarders know the hidden refuges, the handy hiding places, the concealed doors. They are *educated on the inside*, so to speak. They know exactly where you can steal a kiss, which doors don't close well, and which ones can on the other hand conceal all their secrets. Anyone can go in, but you have to be *on your toes* and find the keys.

*

The boarders have a very particular relationship with time: they live in their own time, rebellious and badly regulated, a time that defies time, a war machine that fights the calendar.

Their use of time is full of mysteries: they spend the greater part of their days surveying the corridors, the classrooms, the library, the stairways… They are floating reader heads, mobile microprobes, whose sensitivity is increased by their long years of solitude. When night comes, they move around the arteries of the Lycée like the black flow of blood in the veins. They have an organic vision of the composition of the buildings, of their activity, of how they function. All night, they pass through the Lycée like travelers of the shadows invited by an invisible god. They even walk on the roofs. They have touched the lightning conductor, gone through the dark hallways… Below the magnificence of the outward appearances, they know. They know that all over the Lycée, the plaster is falling apart, the stone is falling, the facings are collapsing. It is not only that the benches are worm-eaten and that the varnish is peeling off. The locks and the ironwork, the masonry and the joinery: there are problems everywhere.

The boarders know *from the inside* the truth of beings and places. In an instant, they pass as they wish from one side of life to the other. They see the reverse side of things. They know the real work of time. It is an internal knowledge, that of the heart, that of breathing. They know that at all times everything is at risk of collapse. And that the thing is to live each moment on its crest to delay the shipwreck of time.

At the Lycée, everybody projects themselves into the future: they think only of tests and competitive exams and everything is directed toward that end, a line that at once guides and marks a horizon. But the boarding school resists this alignment. You live there in a sort of constitutive dynamism, of permanent urgency. Urgency is a very particular feeling of time: contrary to what people think, there is no "state of emergency"—that does not exist. Urgency is never a state: it is a form of speed, a priority. It is a way of living that accepts no delay, and which pushes you forward at all times.

Later, notably in Japan, I will learn to live in a calmer, almost serene sentiment of time, where each day and each night do not transform into unrest. But for now, in the boarding school, we live each day like it was the first and each night like it was the last. We repeat to ourselves the words of Breton, underlined in red by François' own hand in his copy of *Manifesto of Surrealism*: "Everything is near at hand, the worst material conditions are fine. The woods are white or black, one will never sleep."

*

Friendship is an absolutely singular thing. No two friendships are identical and, just as no two fingerprints are the same, every friendship constructs its own space. Ours was first shaped by the most unusual form of the boarding school.

The boarding school is a very particular headquarters. With the polyphony of its windows, the carnival of its hallways and doors, its procession of laughs and the cavalcade of its stairways, the boarding school is the most accurate symbol of friendship. Many discussions are held there and music rings out late into the night. There always floats toward morning a smell of toasted bread and, toward evening, the wafts of wine. It is the antidote—and at the same time, the odd auxiliary—of the austere observances of study, of the pious devotions of essay writing.

It creates a human kaleidoscope, a sort of forum of the Middle Ages, of a lovers' court, full of games, of miracles, of drug selling and book exchanges. With the result that, if I had to give a definition of friendship—that strange ferret that never lets itself be caught—I would say simply: friendship is a limitless, perpetually decentered space in which silence or laughter reign, and where time seems to at once stop and multiply itself.

4. STRAIGHT, NO CHASER

The two streetlights that frame the entry to the Lycée light up, trying to drown out the charms of the evening as it falls… They are classic Parisian streetlamps: massive feet, cast-iron shaft, a conical lantern with four faces. From the evening star to the morning dew, they keep watch. But they can do nothing against the Chinese pine tree at the entryway, the axis connecting the sky and the land. By day, it stores up the energy of the land and returns it once the sun disappears. From then it is the nighttime that reigns.

Lakanal. Boiling point, effervescence. You literally drown yourself in alcohol. You also go up in smoke each night.

Alcohol preserves the fruits and smoke the meats

François sings over and over, his finger raised toward the sky, smiling mockingly. All sorts of drugs circulate under coats, in jacket lapels and linings. Some fabulous substances… Music is everywhere. In J-C's bedroom, at night, the shadows dance. We are rarely in a normal state, I have to say… Our way of living would immediately stupefy every conventional type of person.

*

First of all, there's the alcohol. It is the most straightforward, the easiest. On this subject, we follow the customs of the Persians. François, who spends his days reading Greek historians, found a remarkable passage in Herodotus's *Histories*. After having described the conflict that set the Persians against the Lydians, Herodotus writes: "The Persians have the habit of deciding, when they are drunk, on the most important questions. The decisions taken in this state are submitted to them the following day when they have regained their lucidity, by the master of the house where their deliberations take place. If, when sober, they take the same decisions, they apply them: if not, they reject them. Conversely, when they have first discussed an issue when sober, they take it up again when drunk." An excellent principle! From the 5th century before Christ, but still relevant today. We adopt it straight away. I apply it still today for every somewhat difficult question.

You see a bit of everything passing round at the boarding school. Grande Champagne, Petite Champagne, Folle Blanche, Absinthe with its green pillars… Ratafia from Charente, Floc de Gascogne, soum-soum from Casamance… Sloe gin… All the distillates and the filtrates, the muscatels and the dark reds… We don't mix them up much—each alcohol has its own merits, each night is its own night—but we sometimes come across some strange synergies, some odd hybridizations, some sublime intermixing: Scotch and heather honey, triple sec with coriander, sake with juniper berry leaves, Tsingtao scented with iris. Music: drunkenness enters you simultaneously through hearing and seeing. The raucous drumming of rum, the sonorous cymbals of cognac and Armagnac, the undulating oboes of palm wine.

Then it all spins out of control, propelling into the depths, into the ethers… It is the spiral, the domino. "The port wine effect," as Proust said: "I had already drunk a good deal of port wine, and if I now asked for more it was not so much with a view to the comfort which the additional glasses would bring me as an effect of the comfort produced by the glasses that had gone before." Time becomes a great rolling phenomenon with no beginning or end. One day we will need to come out of it, but for the moment we drink, carried away, rolling through time.

*

You might perhaps ask where we find the time to work in this spiraling cavalcade of music and alcohol. No problem. Everyone at the boarding school knows the advice of Alfred Jarry's philosophy professor in preparing for an exam: "Do nothing, study nothing, read nothing or read only pointless or entertaining subjects that have nothing to do with the test that you are taking."

"Don't ever work," Debord's famous phrase sits enthroned above my desk. "Never working requires great talent," written in pen on a sheet of paper, above François'. We make a hell of a duo.

But the situation is subtler, more complex than that. In each of these alcoholic drinks there is a relationship to work. Take for example Pascal the Athenian. Ouzo is his thing. He drinks at least a liter of it each day, in the evenings in his bedroom with pistachios from Aegina, where he went every year to stock up. But he is also unbeatable on Greek metrics: dactyls, holodactyls, the twelve trochaic cesuras for every seven penthemimers, he knows it all. He goes through the day declaiming spondaic lines and bucolic diereses, scanning in every possible way perispomenes and proparoxytones. It is as if he were transmitting the night's ouzo into a clear poetry, an insuperable prosody.

"The scent of wine, oh much more agreeable, laughing, praying, celestial, and more delicious it is than that of oil!" François invokes Rabelais to theorize the power of wine as a *laboratory*: "There are two kinds of work," he says "one that smells of oil and the other that smells of wine. In the preface to *Gargantua*, Rabelais explains that certain writers work with an oil lamp set on their desk, and others with a glass of wine within arm's reach. That is exactly right! In Lakanal, we are on the side of wine. We are the class of Rabelais!"

*

Some evenings, the debate over Bordeaux and Bourgogne wines goes on long into the night: the glasses clink, the arguments go back and forth, colliding with each other. Other times, we bring a cocktail back to life by lifting it from a book. We burn, for example, on a little spoon heated up by a cigarette lighter, a bit of golden yellow sugar and some vermouth, that is then poured onto crushed ice: a full-on hot and cold effect that is the Lautréamont.

We talk about the meaning of Monk's tune, *Straight, No Chaser*, that plays on a loop every night in its various versions. Orchestra, trio, piano solos, bossa nova reprise: it is always the same tune but, curiously, it is unique and different each time. François explains the title to an already very tipsy gathering:

"*Straight*, that means pure, when you're talking about a drink: for example, a whisky without water or ice."

"And *Chaser*, what is that?"

"It's a non-alcoholic or lower alcohol drink that you have after a strong alcoholic drink. You get it?"

"Like a lemonade after a beer?"

"In our case, more like a port after a whisky…"

"*Straight, No Chaser*. That means then, a glass of pure alcohol, with nothing else on the side."

"That's it: the simple, undiluted elegance of a glass of pure alcohol."

"But what has that to do with the music?"

"Excellent question."

"Does Monk make pure music?"

"In a way. You take a simple, elegant phrase, and you develop it in many ways, different and unique each time."

"Like the *Goldberg Variations*?"

"That's it!"

"You mean to say you drink like Bach composes?"

"Exactly."

The remark fills him with joy: his eyes always light up when he is thinking about music, as if he was leaving for another world while being with us at the same time. He pours himself another drink. Straight, No Chaser, of course.

*

In *To Discern a Flatterer from a Friend*, Plutarch establishes a difference between the friend and the flatterer. It is difficult, he recalls, to distinguish between a real friend and a base flatterer when the latter is particularly hypocritical, false, or dissembling. And yet, Plutarch tells us, there is an easy way to break out the truth: wine.

The flatterers, the false friends, are never on the side of wine: "No, most of the time, he won't drink to excess, but will keep his wits about him; he is prying and inquisitive, would mix in your business, and wind himself into your secrets: in short, he who acts the friend, not with the air of a comedian or a satirist, but with the port and gravity of a tragedian." Or again: "It is true that these people, fleeing the risk of being found out in laughter, pure wine, jests and sarcasms, give to their enterprise an air of gravity." The Greeks were not wrong: they placed friendship on the side of comedy, that is to say, of laughter, dance, and shared wine.

Plutarch was born in Chaeronea, a town situated between Phocis and Attica and not far from the Cephissus River, in the center of Hellas. In chant II of the *Iliad*, it is presented as the land of "bountiful vineyards": suffice to say he knows what he is talking about… He was not unaware that friendship reveals itself especially in laughter, its breathy adventures. And in wine, the pure wine of friendship that we so loved.

*

For *Straight, No Chaser* is not only a way of drinking, playing, and composing. It is also a way of living: ironic, caustic, cheerful.

François is not sentimental. He does not poeticize, does not idealize. He believes in neither effusiveness, nor meditation, nor confidence. The bruising effects of ego, tenderness, "sentiment," mean little to him. That is at least what he likes you to think. He quotes the profound saying that Baudelaire takes from Leconte de Lisle: "All who eulogize are scoundrels." If you are unhappy, you don't say it, you keep it to yourself. The open display of states of mind is, in the proper sense of the word, *lamentable*.

It was at this time that he invented the "theory of the dry method" by drawing on—with a certain irony—the process for manufacturing textiles. Attention: the technical part, explained by him little by little with lots of hand movements, the left resting on the piano as a back-up, the right held out in front like the nose of an airplane. To make certain textiles, there are two methods: the dry method and the wet method. The latter consists of kneading and then diluting the fibers in a very large quantity of water to make a paste. The process makes for textiles that are very homogenous and very firm, with fibers that are extremely measured and uniform. By contrast, following the dry method, the fibers are transported then dispersed in an airflow, firstly across perforated rotating cylinders, then above a cloth with an inbuilt vacuum system. It is an aerodynamic process: the fly ash is filtered and there is no residual liquid effluent. It is quicker, more difficult, more dangerous. It is this method that he prefers, it is the life he has chosen for himself.

It is a similar thing for alcohol. You *drink dry*, as he says—that is, quickly and well, with no hanging around, without procrastination, with no nonsense. Like Gustave Leonhardt, like Thelonius Monk: using only the wrist.

Against teary sentimentality and psychologism, François believes in music and prosody. He studies the playing of his favorite musicians, above all Monk and Leonhardt, incessantly. For jazz, Monk seems to him unsurpassable: chest straight or curved backward, fingers held flat like sticks, he bounces from key to key, unravels then starts over, carrying you with him over there, to the other side of the sounds, in an incalculable series of harmonics. Unpredictable technique of accents, hands crossed, science of the fingers. Monk never takes off his rings, even when he plays: the rings, the fingernails, skin calluses like nerve endings beneath the phalanges, everything is part of this heterogenous and imponderable playing that transports you into a whirl of atoms where life and art seem at each moment to palpitate and spin around each other. You don't plug the gaps, the fissures, you learn to dance above them like the acrobat at the edge of the abyss, black, white, horn, ivory, on the cliffsides of the keyboard.

For classical music, it is Leonhardt. What relationship is there between the turbulent American pianist and the austere Dutch harpsichordist? Between the jazzman and his unusual playing style, garnished with sonic nuggets and the virtually unruffled interpreter of the masterpieces of *The Well-Tempered Clavier*? For François, these are two sides of the same coin: the dry method.

When he plays, Leonhardt is remarkably static as much as Monk is restless: his back does not budge, nor do his legs, nor barely do his wrists. His fingers by contrast undulate like a mechanism made of ball bearings or cogged parts. Monk is cat-like, scratchy, agile, and enraged. Leonhardt has all the look of a rake, perfectly stiff, thin, his hair well-combed. Moreover, it is what he does, tirelessly: he rakes up, he harvests, he tows—and germinates into the open air a whole blossoming of crystalline notes. He is a gardener of the invisible. His playing is fine and precise like a blade, and it is incredible the number of galleries he opens up, of orchards he makes spring up.

Everything has been said and written about the great Leonhardt, about his playing, like a diamond cutter inset with intelligence and rigor, severity and probity. But few today are still sensitive to his humor, to his malice even, that slide discreetly into a playing style that seems constricted. Put a child near to a recording and watch: very quickly, their arms open up, their head leans forward and they smile, the notes of the harpsichord land on the child like petals from a cherry tree. Leonhardt is not the austere high priest that he has often been compared to: look at how his fingers nibble the keyboard, listen to how his sharp notes bring out Bach's mischievous air, a touch of powder over the cantatas, a pinch of salt on the sonatas.

François is particularly sensitive to a gesture, the one with which at that time Leonhardt ended all his concerts: at the point of the last bar, just before the curtain falls and the stage closes over again, before the immense space opened up by the flying Dutchman retreats and disappears back behind the scenes of the event, Leonhardt has a gesture, almost imperceptible and yet recurrent. On the last note, in a movement of great elegance, his right hand moves to the right and becomes rounded like the back of a cat. Then, gently, he places the final finger on the keyboard; then, as the note dies and silence returns, he makes it revolve, turns it round and lifts it again slowly. At the end, his hand is facing the sky, his palm flat, total silence for just a moment before the applause rains down. In the silence that follows the last note, this uncanny emptiness where everything resonates, where death already reinstalls itself, Leonhardt wishes to hold for as long as possible the benediction of music, its final grace.

"It is a royal gesture," François tells me: *Straight, No Chaser*. Beauty is found everywhere, in a great economy of means or, on the contrary, in an exuberant set of body movements. It knows how to be at once exquisite and radical. It has but one enemy, conformism, and a single ally, freedom.

Get yourself drunk. Wine makes the eye clearer and the ear sharper. I have always been wary of people who don't drink. Or even, who drink little. Rabelais called them the abstemious, and associated them with the agelastics: those who never laugh. It is understood that those who drink too much are heavy, coarse: it is all a question of finesse, balance, agility.

But "alcohol, when it goes down well, allows you to come out of yourself and brings about a general dis-enclosure," as our friend Hervé the Nietzschean proclaims in the corridors. I like this fine word, dis-enclosure. Hervé continues, cigarette in one hand and a glass in the other, like Jesus between the two thieves: "To be drunk is to renounce all form of mastery, all barriers, all safeguards: discourse, analysis, memory, morality, limits, norms, rules, economy, inhibitions, identity, postures. Everything flows, flees, overflows, zigzags, everything is carried in all directions at once."

And this disorder, which one might have thought would hold for barely a fortnight, continued week after week, month after month, for two long and beautiful years. Two years in the flames, intense, unconventional, illegal, *against all expectations*.

5. THE BLACK PEARL

Sanctions were not slow in arriving. Like alcohol, we are volatile and dangerous. The administration was quickly on to us, calling the boarding school "a foyer of insubordination." Two warders are hired as reinforcements. The margaux-Monk and whisky-Leonhardt nights are prohibited. The principal sends out a furious memo against these evenings "where the rules of good taste are no less ignored than the laws of morality" and calls out for a "severe repression." In a letter addressed to the families, he laments "these young people who are endowed with quite remarkable means, but who waste their undoubted intellectual qualities with a negative attitude from which the good order of the Lycée has suffered on more than one occasion." The tyrannical virtues are unleashed on the poor boarders. We are "weeds" to be quickly cleared, pulled up, rooted out! Health, security, morality! Salubrity! Tranquility!

Maybe we were "weeds," but we smoked some good stuff. From the spring of the first year in fact, J.-C. began to bring long black, blue, and green branches back to the boarding school. It is our response to the school's reprimand. In this, we without doubt overstepped the mark.

*

Hashish. At Lakanal, we call it "the Pascaline" or "the Memorial." In memory of Blaise Pascal, of course. Pascal, as is well known, always carried with him a parchment covered in notes in condensed handwriting in black ink like flashes of lightning sewn into the lining of his doublet and written on the feverish night where he met up with Christ. It is his breastplate, his shield: under the row of buttons and the tight leather, reserves of incandescent ecstasy. To have always your dose on you, within hand's reach.

The reference to Pascal's conversion may seem incongruous, even sacrilegious. In our minds, it was not. There is religion in hashish, and that is why it has had a hold on men for so long. "We have faith in poison/We know how to give our whole life every day," wrote Rimbaud. To give your whole life, every day, that is the program. Blasphemous? Let's say instead: an illumination. Moreover François, who has always admired the Catholic liturgy, finds in his readings the celebration of a ceremony in honor of the Virgin Mary that uses cannabis in a ritualistic way: the doctrine of Saint Mary, a Brazilian cult. We devote therefore a Marian cult to Mary Jane.

Smoking is really useful as it sets the imagination on a journey. We tried everything: *ketama* from the Rif, *charas* from the Himalayas, *garda* from Afghanistan, Hispanic marijuana, *ganja* from India, and *da ma* from China. We tour the world on the shoulders of Mary Jane. And we see it in all colors: the olive green of the Afghan, the lavender of Holland, the licorice of the Himalayan, the sandy *aya* , the red of Lebanon… All the historians—of weed—will tell you: from migration to migration, from millennium to millennium, hemp spins its web everywhere. The Iranians and the Chinese, the Hebrews, the Egyptians and the Indians, the Arab, Asian, English, and Venetian merchants, all of them transported it in their nets between the fabrics for clothing, the medicine for curing oneself, the paper to write on, and the dried flowers to take flight. Since the Sumerian tablets, languages everywhere have retained traces of it, obscure and perfumed, from Sanskrit to Tamil, from Egyptian to Portuguese.

There is something for every taste and it comes in all sizes: the stick (a leaf), the duet (two leaves), the trinity (three leaves), the clover (four leaves), the fifth (five leaves), the sextet (six leaves), the alexandrine (twelve leaves)—and the monstrous sixteen-leaves, which only the grand masters like Vincent the Pilgrim can handle.

An atmosphere of stalks of weed, the cracking of lighters. You light the wick and the joint is passed round: "Beloved, think it not strange concerning the fiery trial which is to try you, as though some extraordinary thing happened unto you" (our friend Marco recites the first epistle). And it is true, we rise to the skies in a few minutes.

The tobacco is rolled, the fingers strum, the mouth embraces the paper. These are very simple gestures, but endowed with a great grace. The flame rises: the world is all around us now with a singular force. Suddenly, we see very clearly the bright parts, the dark parts, the differences in depth in the space of the bedroom or the differences in distances between bodies, the contrasts that become more marked between neighboring objects. Colors take on a particular vividness.

But what strikes you is above all sound, the enlargement of the space by sound. The air fills up with syntagms and an uninterrupted burst of strangely-flavored phonemes. *Spliff*, *high*, *skunk*, the monosyllables crackle, the joint goes round, the waves travel. At night, the *special queen* unravels her charms and dances the length of the walls. *Skunk* unfurls in the higher parts. Take cover, the Pope has just arrived in the *shelter*. He is carrying in the lining of his chasuble a few grams of *weed* and some tufts of *blow*. All that echoes loudly onto the streets, into the night outside... The tenses themselves are overturned: the present falls away, the conditional is surpassed, the past historic revisited. The drawer of the imperfect undergoes a considerable extension. The slightest phrase takes on a surprising shape and a meaning that is sometimes very far from its normal sense. The whole prairie opens up before us: we become aware of all that can happen in a succession of vowels and consonants.

François turns toward J.-C. and quotes Robert Bresson, one

of his favorite filmmakers: "When a sound can replace, suppress or neutralize an image, the ear goes more to the inside, the eye to the external." He is completely right. The internal ear and the piercing eye.

Then, the girls enter the dance. They inject their quivering voices into the cadences of jazz. Melpomene undulates and Thalia sways her hips. Mr. Tambo and Mr. Bones are on percussion and set the refrain free in a crash of knucklebones. The narration progresses by jerks, kicks, bouts of laughter, and sonic elements that until now were separated suddenly place themselves at our disposal. A theme is introduced, then developed, twisted and imperceptibly modified until, though remaining recognizable, it becomes completely different. Syncopations, vocalizing... It is the school of rhythm. Morphemes follow one after the other, producing a new meaning. The phrase refuses all hierarchies, it is a great uncontrollable melody: you see propositions floating in the piece, groups of words that join up together under a hail of bifurcating conjunctions, prepositions in single file, vast cascades of verbs that overturn each other, a series of splendid and inexhaustible signs.

Our supplier is J.-C. Jean-Claude, known as Jacky la Coke or Jesus Christ. Round spectacles, little gray chin beard, the breathy voice of the serious smokers. And always his long sweaters from his pilgrimages round his neck. J.-C. is the globalized apostle of dope, the narcotic cosmopolitan. Supremely cultured, kind, intelligent. He travels round the world all year and brings his latest international discoveries back to the boarding school. He knows all there is to know about hashish: he is a walking encyclopedia, a multilingual dictionary of the bronchi and the brushlands, a true library of the lungs.

"*Purple haze* is clear and vigorous: a laser. Its secret lies in contrast: the perfume is very delicate but the taste is very dense. It is this chiaroscuro that is its strength. Here, pass along the joint…" He holds out his hand and catches the reefer. "But the best hashish is the *zamal* of the Indian Ocean. Simply, you need to know the vintages and to get to know the *gramounes*, the old mountain people who have grown it for centuries." He stands up, takes a puff then brings out a very nice green branch from his closet. "Look, this one is a native, a vintage… I took it back from around Cilaos, on La Réunion. It took me hours to find it. These are very old plants grown in the highlands close to the sky, according to ancestral methods. Which means they get plenty of oxygen and ultraviolet rays: it's good stuff! Today, with their genetic mixing at every stage and their manufactured flavors, their synthetic by-products, they have lost the taste of the authentic… Have a blast of that…"

The purple mist fills up the room, mixed with the blue-green color of the sickle thorn plant. "There are many varieties of it: this one with its vanilla and cinnamon accents must be quite close in taste to the *dawamesk*, the hashish marmalade eaten by Baudelaire, Gautier, Nerval and the others at the Hashischins Club. Here, pass the doobie around… As they ingested it instead of smoking it, the effect must have been all the more powerful. You will see Zanzibar…"

Indeed… Very quickly, it is "the clarinet" as J.-C. says, a whole orchestra of sensations. First, a slither of light, you see waves and sands, then the skies open up and are set ablaze. Then, large limbs appear, lime or dark green. You are sitting down but have the impression of lying stretched out in the middle of a forest. Soon, the girls are hot and undress… It is the luncheon on the grass!

"Did you see how quick the effects are?" J.-C. asks with a large smile that begins to seriously distort his lower lip. "All of a sudden, it comes, without warning… As far back as 1860,

Baudelaire wrote..." He holds out his arm toward his library that seems very far away, on the other side of the bed, but which comes to him with incredible speed, like a magnet. In next to no time, the book is open on his knees and he reads: "This marvelous state has no symptoms in advance. *It is as unexpected as a ghost.*" He stresses these final words. We become ghosts, then. You float... you glide, you navigate... you emerge in the middle of orange clouds with girls in their bras... Landing softly between cinnamon cherry trees and lilac guava trees.

J.-C., clearly as addicted to Baudelaire as he is to Mary Jane, carries on reading while drawing on his cigarette: "Yet the opium had produced its usual effect, which is to cloak the external world with an intensity of interest. In the trembling of a leaf, in the color of a blade of grass, in the shape of a clover, in the humming of a bee, in the splash of a dew drop, in the sigh of the wind, in the vague odors that escape from the forest, is produced a whole world of inspirations, a magnificent and multicolored procession of disordered and rhapsodic thoughts."

He reads well in his hazy, soft voice. An immediate erotic effect is guaranteed in the bedroom. It is the power of the Herb, venomous and proliferating. Sensitivity is heightened, from the stalk to the tip. Girls are flowers or twigs, boys are leaves, foliage. Hands take a walk over the headlands, you embrace in the skies, kisses like cascades, teeming and profound.

"Last year, I went to China," J.-C. continues, having closed the book but holding it still in his hands like a missal. "I tasted there some *gunpowder*: hashish leaves mixed with tea leaves. They call that "cannon powder," not for its strength but because the leaves are rolled into little balls. It is a semi-fermented mountain hashish. The people of Hangzhou call it the hashish of the Great Red Dress as it provokes hallucinations, or the Dragon's hashish, as it lets you straddle the clouds. It gives you a real hit:

you feel like you have flipped over to the other side of things..." As he says that, he stretches out across the knees of the girl next to him, who strokes his hair gently.

J.-C. has put the book down, he recites by heart now between two puffs, intoning, chanting:

Beneath tobacco-smoke clouds, hiding the ceiling,
Through the book's subtle mystery, always leafing...

A little to the side, close to the window, François glides on high in the Milky Way... A cigarette in the mouth, he hums a cantata. He always stands like that for a long time, contemplating the moon, space, the immense night before us. He observes the vault, the constellations... He knows them all, he points them out and names them: Cassiopeia, Andromeda, Pegasus, and Delphinus...

His favorite is Orion. The three stars in the center, so bright, equidistant, and perfectly aligned. "Like the Three Wise Men," he says. And then Orion's quadrangle, Saiph, Bellatrix, Betelgeuse the red, and Rigel the blue. Pigments of the infinite... He really would like to catch them, bring them into the room, all these starry dustings. Later, he would install in his room a telescope and he would have this strange saying: "The telescope is like hashish, a means of seeing at once farther and more precisely..."

J.-C., who always has more than one piece of weed in his bag, then gets up and goes to rummage in his closet. Deeper over there, behind the piles of sweaters he bought on his latest trip to Nepal... "I didn't take anything back from China last year, it was too dangerous. But this summer, I went to Afghanistan. And there..." he rummages a bit more... he knows how to keep you hanging there, in suspense. His arm digs deep, the forearm then the elbow, right down to his shoulder, all of his arm now in darkness as if it has been sucked up by the closet, even deeper he goes, under the jerseys and jumpers, it is his hiding place, his secret stash… "Here it is!" He pulls out a little sealed container kept at constant temperature and coated in black, the size of a cello: a perfect oasis for preservation.

The container is opened up. A religious silence settles over the little bedroom that the wafts of smoke have enlarged to the dimensions of a cathedral. Everyone stares wide-eyed to see the trove better in the darkness. For it is not one but two immense branches that have come out of the container. The first is green and luminous, luxuriant and bushy like a sheaf of jade. "It is *Afghan kush*, the famous AK-47," J.-C. explains, with a huge smile spreading upwards across his face right to the tips of his ears. Watch now, this is not your usual stuff that they sell in Paris under the same name, it is *roots*, it comes straight out of the ground! It has the name of a Russian assault rifle, but you will see, it is quite sweet and sugary…"

Vincent the Pilgrim rolls a beautiful six-leaf joint and it is only fitting that J.-C. fire the scud missile. The marvel is then passed round the room for a few minutes in a merry-go-round of murmurings and perfumes. It is hazy, round in the mouth, with an aftertaste of almond. Black poplars and poppy seeds, quince pips… In a few minutes, the room has gone from dark green to a lavender color.

The AK-47 sometimes tastes like fruit, sometimes like flowers: it is the guerilla warfare of sweetness. Easy takeoff, rapid trajectory, then the head that changes course midflight, a rotating breech-block and trigger system. At the end of the burst of fire, a displacement of mass toward the rear: it is very good. From time to time you come across a little ball, the nugget: then it fires off like a grenade launcher. You have to take two or three puffs very quickly, rapid pistol fire, and then you get back to the sweetness.

Silence. A glass of water. J.-C. prepares the second branch.

This one is stranger. A lot more worrying. It comes out of the container murmuring, river-like, and as soon as it is there everyone stares at it, as if magnetically affected. The leaves are scalloped-edged and deep black. Suddenly, François has left the window ledge and approaches the fibers palpitating in the shadows:

"What is this thing?"

"The Afghans call it the Black Pearl."

"The Black Pearl?"

"Yes, it is very rare: I don't think you can get it anywhere in France. I bought it in the valley of the Helmand River, south of Kabul. It was grown according to a method that dates back two thousand years... At least, that's what they told me. I made a joint from it earlier, but I didn't dare light it. I prefer to smoke it when there are others around. Its smell is amazing, as you will see..."

The leaves of the Afghan are black like carbon with glints of oil, a black so intense that its color is hard to look at with the naked eye. It digs a hole in the bedroom. By contrast, the walls seem more and more distant, more and more white, more and more flat... Black hashish literally vaporizes the room as it enters it. It is a dull, tense, tragic black. All of us have gathered round the joint, waiting there as if on the edge of an abyss.

J-C. lights up the spliff... A white smoke spurts out with a delicious perfume of coriander. Gradual lift-off. Little by little, curves unwind and arabesques unfurl in twists and coils... A soft drug is like a tree growing: it is always shifting. Journey to the inside of the thorax. And then without warning, something brutal, something extraordinarily violent: you go into a space where you can no longer see anything. Your consciousness of time evaporates. Identity, space, calendars, everything is literally pulverized. The room rocks in the grip of some hidden force, of some *irreversible* blackness. You enter the pure world of sensation.

A poppy smell rises across the room and sets the throat alight with a savage thirst. In the middle of the bedazzlement is a sudden terror. This is the time of the Assassins! Horror takes the place of beauty. You go through the whole range of surprises: you are successively crushed, cooked, kneaded, molded, dried. Knives cut shadows on the walls of the bedroom. And then, explosions. They always come in twos and repeat themselves endlessly: *bang bang*, straight into the vortex, all the more so as J.-C. is giving us doses that would tear a tiger's brain to pieces.

Then, Antoine makes a "closet." That is, he breathes in a large quantity of smoke and holds it in his rib cage for thirty seconds. The effect is complete stupor. In the middle of the room, a man stands alone, leaning slightly. No one knows him, no one knows how he came to be there. But it's him, Antoine. He steps forward, he opens his mouth. He has a deep, cavernous voice. He speaks: "I am the crow with the monstrous beak from the fairy tales…" He came out of one of those enormous eggs that peasants find sometimes near mountains. Now he speaks, he speaks, and nothing can stop him. He wants to go to Fontevraud Abbey to settle the score with the enemies of the Plantagenets. His giant beak will smash them, break their skulls down to the marrow, open them up then pull out their ears, pull out their intestines! He spreads the plague, it's a great disaster… He is a man, but not a man. A bird, but not a bird. A dog, but not a dog. He has the hands of a human, the head of a wolf, a pair of wings, and can walk, run or fly as he pleases…

The night is ending and the day is about to begin. Soon, the dawn comes and you find yourself wandering over a moor. You are searching for the black nightshade, for those who find some can go to the sabbath to meet the devil. The road is dark and tortuous, sinuous. If you have the misfortune to come across a mirror, above all do not provoke it. The face in the mirror becomes deformed and grows bigger. The lips, the eyes, the teeth, the tongue... Leaning over the basin, you dissolve as on contact with water.

Then, comes the last phase: joy. Since he smoked the Black Pearl, François has been immensely joyful. His nostrils dilate, he has extraordinary, voracious nostrils, which sniff merrily: when he leans over the hashish, the sensors on his nose twitch like a dragonfly hovering over a reed. He breathes it all in, he literally sails over the tobacco.

And me, I can hear my heart beating. I can even hear the sound made by each of our hearts, each second, the little human detonation, the double beating of time. I can hear the human noise that we make, sitting and immobile, the song of blood in the veins, even when the room falls into darkness. I suddenly understand that we had inside us worlds that existed on their own, that fire and smoke are made from a single, vigorous, mortal gesture. It is the lesson of the black hashish: pearls of joy set themselves free, they leap outside of our rib cages in flows, gulps, puffs. We had them inside us and we did not know it.

It is night, a night like all the others at the Lycée Lakanal. Then, in the silence that falls again before the next blast-off, someone reads aloud the prospectus that is sent to the pupils' parents every year: "Every floor has a small kitchen equipped with a microwave oven and a refrigerator. This equipment is to be used for the preparation of hot drinks during the long evenings of study. Each evening a team of masters from the school ensures the maintenance of a studious and agreeable atmosphere."

We laugh. Couples kiss. A last long, sweet, sugary kiss. The night stars come out in their hundreds.

*

Still today, when I think of François, the smoke from a cigarette appears in the room. Always, in every place, at every hour of the day and the night, a white fog floats above his face. He lights his cigarette and inhales a puff. He speaks as he exhales the smoke from his mouth and nose. I have never seen someone smoke a cigarette so intensely. He is literally burning his way through it. And he will soon light up another one. François is like that: a combusting being.

It is the art of the spiral: something is burning. We need to burn; we are burning. François pushed a certain idea of life that involved taking risks, taking flight, an explosion to the limit. He had in him happiness which he smoked, drank, and burned deeply, fully.

It would take a wave one December day in the Canaries, a huge, mad, villainous wave to finally extinguish this will-o'-the-wisp, this phenomenal combustion.

*

Why does a friendship develop? Who can say...? And why do friends so often come in pairs? As far back as *To Discern a Flatterer from a Friend,* Plutarch notes that "friendship is an animal that grazes in pairs." In saying that, the Greek thinker is referring to the pairs of friends that appear everywhere in ancient Greek mythology and that are one of the few means we have, even today, of representing the enigma of a friendship: Achilles and Patroclus, Castor and Pollux, Orestes and Pylades are the best known. But there are also Theseus and Pirithous, Pythias and Damon, Heracles and Iolaus... Some very rich material! Powerful, too, as it crosses the centuries and survives to the present day, even if it is in a comic and degraded form: Laurel and Hardy (the burlesque version), Bouvard and Pécuchet (the grotesque version)...

Friendship exists first between two people or not at all.

This eulogy to the duo is not only a literary myth. It is illustrated in numerous examples from real life: Tacitus and Pliny the Younger, Dante and Cavalcanti, Ronsard and Du Bellay, Goethe and Schiller—and a pair of friends who remain the best, almost unbeatable example, Montaigne and La Boétie.

It also seems to be found in different countries as in the example, too little known in France, of Du Fu and Li Bai, the two most celebrated poets of the Tang Dynasty. Du Fu and Li Bai met at Luoyang, between the Luo River and the Yellow River, in the year 740. Luoyang was then one of the biggest cities in the country and the capital of the East. It was the time of the Tang and there was no shortage of men of letters. Suffice to say that Du Fu and Li Bai might well not have met and, even if their paths had crossed, they might never have been able to find one another again.

What do Du Fu and Li Bai actually have in common? Almost nothing. They are as different as Yin and Yang: Li Bai is a very well-known poet; Du Fu is a failed civil servant. Du Fu is a Confucianist with a very strong social conscience, Li Bai is an inveterate drunkard. They say he writes ten poems per liter of wine. Li Bai's style is most often lyrical and free, joyous and impulsive, spontaneous. The poems of Du Fu are quite epic and somber, heavy and rigid in form. Even their endings are radically different: Du Fu dies in poverty and sickness, completely consumed by his art. The death of Li Bai is a lot more bizarre: according to the legend, drunk on a small boat, he sees the reflection of the moon on the water and drowns trying to catch it. He dies by drowning, like François.

What connects Du Fu and Li Bai is, however, a lot stronger than what separates them: a very strong love for wine and travel, but above all for poetry. Their companionship would last only two years, but the poems that they exchanged remain, more than a thousand years later, among the finest in the Chinese language.

The poetic sensibility is the best gauge of the possibility of friendship. It has never to my knowledge been noticed, but it is on friendship that Isidore Ducasse both opens and closes his collection *Poésies*, many centuries later. In the burst of dedications that open the volume, you notice in fact this one, in capital letters:

> TO FRIENDS, past, present, and future

Then, a few lines from the end, this very beautiful phrase:

> *So long as my friends do not die*
> *I will not speak of death.*

Isidore Ducasse is right: it is our friends who keep us from death. And it is friendship that gives us the key to poetry.

Toward the end of his life, following a dark episode of plotting and rebellion typical of Chinese history, Li Bai is exiled in the Yelang in the south, near to Guizhou. It is at that time a region ravaged by malaria and, even today, one of the poorest parts of the country.

Du Fu is worried about his friend and, one night, sees him in a dream. He awakens and rises but continues to see him in a corner of the room, so close to him that he could touch him. He thinks about Qu Yuan, another banished poet who committed suicide by throwing himself in the River Miluo and who composed in his fever the following two strangely premonitory lines:

> *The waters are deep, the waves savage*
> *Watch out for the dragons from the depths*

Thirteen centuries have passed. François died by drowning like Li Bai. I often see him in my dreams, and it breaks my heart not to have been able to say to him:

The waters are deep, the waves savage
Watch out for the dragons from the depths

*

Recto Verso
Yin Yang
Vice versa
Heads and tails
Duo duel
One and the other
Side by side
Stage left stage right
Forehand backhand
As thick as thieves

"We were like teeth and lips," says Godard about his friendship with Truffaut in a strange, faintly disgusting expression. But when Truffaut dies, he comes out with this surprising phrase: "François is perhaps dead. I am perhaps alive. There is no difference, right?"

*

Friends, then, two by two, until death do they part. There is a mathematical element to friendship.

Petrarch always knew what he was talking about regarding the complex ballet of numbers and feelings as it was he for example who proposed to make "Varron's law" on meals a more general principle. What is Varron's law? A precept of the knight Varron, who was responsible for the organization of the first public libraries in Rome. So that a dinner might be a perfect success, he recommends finding the right number of guests. His advice is, it seems to me, still valid: "We recommend among other things that the number of guests be no greater than that of the Muses and not less than that of the Graces so as not to fall into one of those two extremes – crowd or solitude – even if, in my opinion, one must always tend toward solitude." Between the Muses and the Graces, that is to say between nine and three people, is the right number for a successful dinner.

At Lakanal, they call the handful of friends that hang around François "La Petite Bande," The Little Gang. La Petite Bande is the name of a musical ensemble specializing in baroque music using period instruments and a direct reference to the king's Petite Bande des Violons, Lully's orchestra at the court of Louis XIV. It was founded by the astonishing Kuijken brothers (Sigiswald on the violin, Wieland on the viola da gamba, and Barthold on the flute) and Gustav Leonhardt. A trident and its scepter. Given our taste for baroque music, La Petite Bande is a particularly well-chosen name.

It is all a question of numbers, not figures. When Petrarch says that "friendship is an animal that grazes in pairs," he is also alluding to Plato's myth, for whom the collectivity was a "large animal" locked into its cave and following only shadows. To get out of the cave, there is nothing better than a friend. When things are going badly, while the shadows drag you down and false friends stir like simulacra gesticulating on the cave walls, it is the friend who will help you back to the surface.

It is the little animal against the "big animal." The multiplication of the small animals makes for a swarm of friends. In twos, from three to five, rarely more, up to a maximum of nine. Here we are far from the idea of friendship as a "social link," the foundation or condition of the possibility of "living together"—even if these components can also contribute to it, they are but its most exterior part, its varnishing. Friendship is deeper, an obscure part tied up with its inmost depths.

Friends do not travel in troupes or groups. Against the mania for cliques or clans, for the brotherhood as a lobby group, a colony, a coterie, a nation or a block of houses. Friendship is not a crowd: friendship is a "little gang."

PART TWO: *LIBERA ME*

1. THE BERTRAND STUDIO

Return to Montmartre, evening.

Now that little by little I am crossing backwards the times we spent together, I realize that those two years were unique: not only because of the particular qualities of the days and nights there from the late May afternoons until the first lights of dawn, of the memories of snow on the Parc de Sceaux, the walks under Aulnay's leafy shade, searching for the contours of the Bièvre or in the footsteps of Chateaubriand in the Vallée-aux-Loups… But also because they constitute a kind of poetic season where time was never truly defined by the class bell, the course schedule, the waiting for an exam or the result of a test. We were supposed to be preparing ourselves for the most difficult competitive examination in France, that of the École Normale Supérieure, and all we thought of was wandering through the pages of books or in the gardens of the château, smoking strange cigarettes among the titmice, the loves carved in relief, and the winged women. They are unique also because of the strange cocktail of tobacco and alcohol, of literature and nighttime, of sex and laughter, love and freedom: the length of the days, the magnitude of the nights were never traversed by boredom or discouragement. We swam in a space without limits, set free from time. We transformed all the swamplands of study into silvery bursts of water and the hall of residence into a princely domain.

That time is now doubly dead. Not only is it past, but since François' death, it is as if it is under lock and key, confiscated forever. The courses of our lives, our visual transformations, the multiplication of journeys undertaken, of encounters, the changes in countries, friends, jobs, the slow workings of time and all the betrayals of women, of men, of the years, all the vicissitudes of existence seem to have brought it down and buried it forever. Friends themselves have been carried away by this great wave. They are replaced by children, imbecilic colleagues, dimwitted assistants, business partners, distinguished learned friends, disastrous collaborators, perfidious associates… Friends are like years, you never see them again.

Those years seem now lost, out of reach, as if they were on the other side of an abyss. And yet… real friendship ignores time. It is there, it crackles, it palpitates in the shadows. It needs only a chance to fire up again. Friends are precious stones, jewels: you lose sight of them, you forget them, you no longer even know where you put them, and then one day they come out of the box and the miracle reoccurs.

*

The "Rabelais method" has borne its fruits as never before has the Lycée Lakanal had so many candidates eligible to sit the oral exam at the École Normale Supérieure. The class of Rabelais is huge, even if it shrank quickly after the oral exams. We had a series of wild parties after the announcement of the results and the boarders turned up to the oral exams with monumental hangovers that lasted for several days. To everyone's surprise, François himself did not do so well. He was the most brilliant of all of us. I did better, no doubt thanks to the subject I landed with in general culture: "Death in a work of your choice." I chose Céline, who was already somewhat out of favor (he is even more so today). Sink or swim. I swam. But with success as with failure, the whole gang broke up: J.-C. wrapped himself up proudly in his sweater and left again for Pakistan or the Himalayas, others turned to journalism, others to teaching, politics, or business, others still to Rome, the École Nationale d'Administration, or Africa. The divine parenthesis had lasted for two years.

François carried on, continued his literary studies and wrote a fascinating dissertation on Saint-Simon: "The Representation of Power in Saint-Simon's *Mémoires*—year 1715," defended at the University of Paris VII under the supervision of Maurice Laugaa. But university was a bore for him as he had already decided what he wanted to do: his great passion, cinema.

*

Cinema led him to the abyss and he knew it. It has a deathly power about it. You go into a black room and all you meet is darkness, phantoms of feelings. Faces on the screen move in a fake halo, words are spoken, a whitish light comes off the stage and floods the front rows, people meet briefly without touching, they embrace each other without really meaning it, they die without really succumbing, they are never really completely dead or completely alive. It takes all the power of the great filmmakers to take from these mirages a moment of true light, to make of this factory of lies a workshop of truth. Thus, cinema becomes an active ingredient, it unmasks, it pierces the screen and makes people aware of its stupefying power of revelation.

Cinema is darkness. The power of the obscure. The entry into the theater, feeling your way in. The going back in time. Nothing however that is anything like an infantile regression, a sort of pleasure in babbling. But a profound sense of vertigo. A birth remade in reverse, devoured. A means of being reborn to oneself. Today, all theaters look like each other more or less. Before, the entry into the dark room was like the discovery of a grotto. When the screen lights up, it is a tearing, as if you were seeing the sky for the first time. When the lights go up again in the room, you leave the cave and go back out into the fresh air, armed with new weapons for the chase.

Every film is a birth, every film worthy of the name creates at once a dark sign and a strange light. Cinema is an infusion of darkness.

*

However much François loved cinema, he hated nearly all the filmmakers. The only ones he liked were Hitchcock, Godard, Pasolini, Straub and Huillet, and Robert Bresson. Sometimes, he spares a film or two: *Un chien andalou*, obviously. Oshima's *In the Realm of the Senses*. He greatly admires *L'Enfant sauvage*, for its use of music. The whole opening sequence of *L'Enfant sauvage* is strangely silent: all you hear are sounds of nature, the rustling of branches, dogs barking, birds singing. It is the moment where the wolf-child is captured, hidden away in the forest. But when the child frees himself again for a short while, alone in the rain in the courtyard of a farm or walking in the woods, Vivaldi streams in: the *Concerto for Mandolin* and the *Concerto for Piccolo and Strings*, both in C major. "It is the clarity of C major. Truffaut is one of the few filmmakers to have used it. What sweetness in the slowness, what virtuosity in its rapidity… The tightness of the strings, the dreamy flute…" François is ecstatic when he listens to them. "Truffaut, who plays the role of a doctor and teacher in the film, always speaks very quickly, but when the music comes in, he falls silent. No more chat. He learned that from Hitchcock, I think. It is a sign of the greats."

Later, he will add the following to this very personal pantheon: Kubrick, Kiarostami and Lars von Trier. He also loves Méliès and Buster Keaton. He takes an interest in Scorsese from time to time, but less so than in John Cassavetes: "He works like a madman, he prepares... but the result is as fluid as possible. No patter, no chat! Light, sound, filming, framing, reframing, bodies and the relations between these bodies and above all, montage. No ideas! No concepts!"

It is all the same a paradoxical position to love cinema and hate filmmakers. "Not at all," he responds, "it is quite logical." Everyone asks him why. He lights a cigarette, takes a big puff, then explains while exhaling the smoke through his nose. "The problem today is that there are only false films, and that people call these false films, real films."

He gets up and goes to look in his library for *Comments on the Society of the Spectacle* by Guy Debord, which he bought on its release and in which he found this passage: "The government of the spectacle, which now has all the means of falsifying the overall production and general perception, is the absolute master of memory as it is the unregulated master of the projects that shape the farthest future. It reigns alone everywhere: it carries out its summary judgments."

He reads with delectation in a voice that resonates, and adds his own comments in parentheses: "A few examples of falsification: a financier will be a singer (this has been seen), a lawyer will become a police informer (this has also been seen!), a baker will set out his literary preferences (it is the principle of all the literary programs today, François says, exaggerating a little), an actor will govern (plenty of examples of this), a cook will philosophize on the stages of cooking as if they were milestones in universal history..."

He puts the book carefully back on the library shelf. "He is right, Debord. Years ahead. We will see the disappearance of all true competency, you'll see. In the future, writers will make films and directors will make soap operas! People who give their opinions on television will be called writers, and bankers who invest in the film industry will be called filmmakers!"

He stubs out his cigarette in the ashtray and immediately lights up another one. The turbo-prop is in full flow, he carries on: "What's more, you see, all the theaters are closing… Now it is the time of the multiplexes, as they call them. Do you know what a multiplex is? You take eight rooms, you put them all in the same place. And then you take eight different films, but which are really all the same. You have to have a big parking lot (because that is what you are going to do, park the people there, put them in a siding), and preferably a suburban location. Lots of candy and drinks. Confectionery! Comfortable seats. You graze around the place a bit, mess around in all the secondary things. No matter what… And the cinema inside all of that? It doesn't matter!"

He raises and lowers his eyebrows like seismographs. Another cigarette. He is now a Delphic divinity, a raging oracle. A prophet!

"The single-screen, gone! The film as a singular, unique, irreplaceable work: dead, finished, nowhere to be found! It is like in literature where there are more and more *titles* and fewer and fewer *books*. There are more and more *films* and less and less *cinema*. It is the paradox of our time, cinema, literature, everything is variolate."

"*Variolate*? What does that mean?"

"It is the sickness of our time. Everything is more and more varied, and less and less diversified. You can see all of its symptoms: a general eruption of false films, false books, false paintings, all destined to be immediately forgotten. There is more and more variety but less and less choice. It is the variola virus: an invasion of papules, vesicles, pustules of all kinds… The contents become murky, you notice a flattening toward the center and the whole thing is covered in big scabs."

Ah, he is in full flow now. He is angry…

Smoke has taken over the room, but he is right, everything is now becoming clear. He exaggerates, of course, but the problem he raises has only got worse since, "Cinema had everything to be the complete medium yet it has died under the flood of images, the great wave of the chromo, the tide of special effects. Appearances, fascinations… at best illustrations… opinions! That's today's films for you. The amplification of all the senses has given way to the flattening effects of the image. Flat screens, flat films, flat encephalogram."

*

François does not, however, give up on cinema. Quite the contrary. He does not let himself be discouraged. Together, we have a program called "A film a day, seven books a week." It will never be completed, but set on the horizon like a line, it allows us to move forward.

The Bertrand Studio is a little theater built in the 1930s. Situated on a quiet street near to the Rue de Sèvres, in the 7th arrondissement, for a single ticket, you can stay the whole day, from two in the afternoon until midnight. It is there that we go, for hours on end, immersing ourselves. A large building with nine floors. But behind the gray concrete façade it is a mysterious mine hidden under the paneling. I see again the glass canopy at the entrance, the chandelier in the foyer, the sofas of red velvet with burgundy tinges, the metallic balconies and the stalls, the stucco ceiling with its borders, corniches and moldings, the large panoramic screen… At the bar, they have sandwiches and coffee, sometimes onion soup. Bodies brush up against each other, arms touch, eyes meet. You can smoke, which suits François well, and gives to these great dark, purply afternoons the appearance of a dream.

I don't know who was in charge of the programming at the Studio Bertrand, but they were a genius. Every day, they put on a vast, completely surrealist, anarchist, and varied program. Six or seven films for the price of one! But it was above all the discovery of a whole repertoire that was original and personal, extraordinarily varied and incisive, by turns dreamy and fantastic, as poetic as you could want. The films are not classified by genre, period, or theme, they seem moreover not to be classified at all and yet you sense a secret coherence all through this intermittent, continuously renewing epiphany. Every session is a salvo which germinates, develops and blooms, before disappearing and leaving in its wake sounds, words, smiles and smells that haunt you for a long time, hanging in the foggy night air.

The Studio Bertrand is not the only theater where we carry out our investigations: there is also the Rue d'Ulm, the Cinémathèque, Le Champollion, La Pagode... But it is the one that leaves me with the strongest taste, with its feeling of an unexpected recital, of permanent publication, of uninterrupted festivity.

All the Hitchcocks, the Buñuels, the Marx Brothers, the Dreyers, the Murnaus... Eisenstein, Pasolini, Mizoguchi, Rossellini, Antonioni... It is there that we saw *Suspicions* by Hitchcock, *The Invisible Man* by James Whale, *Le Doulos* by Melville, the 1933 *King Kong*, and the Tourneur films on RKO with the mouthwatering titles: *La Griffe du passé*, *La Féline*, and *L'Homme-léopard...* The days and nights pass by in this endless enchantment: the Studio Bertrand is the opposite of a multiplex. Not eight theaters aligned side by side in a row, but eight theaters in one, ten hours in a row, with a considerable hallucinatory power.

In the mid-afternoon, it's *She Wore a Yellow Ribbon*: you go out hunting with Count Zaroff and Feuillade's vampires. In the evening, you come across some eyes without a face, or *A Man Escaped. Vertigo…* Cary Grant looks at us and says: "Everyone wants to be Cary Grant. Even I want to be Cary Grant." While we wait, I am *M. le Maudit* and François *Pierrot le Fou*. Together, we set sail for *Macao* but without forgetting to (re-)watch *A Girl in Every Port*. We are on first-name terms with *Queen Christina* and we touch *The Big Sky*. We go to sleep *Underwater* and wake up with *Montana Belle*. These are dangerous liaisons. At the very end, *His Kind of Woman* and *The Body Snatcher*! By the end of the night, we find ourselves on *La Jetée…*

Given the duration of the screenings and the hallucinatory programming at Studio Bertrand, we often doze off. Nothing is ever set in advance, sleep changes the game and reshuffles the cards, transforming what was but a series of films into a vast kaleidoscope, a universe of shapes in permanent movement. On the fringes of dreams, we find the bridge between sleep and wakefulness. The succession of films but also tiredness, the darkness between reels, the wafts of smoke that drift from the seats to the screen, from the screen to the stalls, from the stalls to the balconies, leave us in a strange state of intense concentration and heightened receptiveness. It is a *projection*, in all the senses of the term: we are propelled into a world where all becomes again enigma, mystery, comprehension. We escape from the televisual to find again a real relationship with perception. All the possibilities of sound and vision emerge from this renewed and as if refreshed.

2. LIBERTY TO THE CAPTIVES

On 23 December 1986, the day before Christmas Eve, the Studio Bertrand closed its doors for good. François calls me right away:

"That's it then, cinema is dead—if it ever existed."

Cinema is dead, it is therefore high time to reinvent it. For a year and a half, François would prepare for the competitive exam for the FEMIS, the great European school of sound and image that he enters in 1988 in the "Filmmakers" section. FEMIS is one of the best schools in the world: it will be important to François. He will gain there a solid knowledge of the trade and also meet some faithful friends such as Renaud Cohen, another atypical filmmaker, who holds a Master's in Chinese and produces documentaries on China and uncategorizable, tender and subtle full-length films. Later, François will work as assistant director on films by Camille de Casabianca, Mehdi Charef, and Alain Cavalier, who is a particular favorite of his. He is well-trained, then.

Time passes and François becomes harder, more piercing. More and more, he loses interest in fiction and traditional cinema, which he now thinks to be an almost completely uninteresting form of entertainment. Only the documentary appears to him still capable of saying something about the world we live in.

It is also at this time that he starts to become a kind of flaneur… He cruises around for long periods, camera in hand, in the so-called "sensitive" housing projects around the Parisian beltway or in the passageways of the metro system. In January 1990, having gone to film the "people of the streets," he meets a group of homeless people at the Châtelet-les-Halles station. In the heart of Paris, in this large station built completely underground, and in almost the same spot where the *Cour des miracles* was situated in the Middle Ages (the Rues de la Grande-Truanderie and de la Petite Truanderie still bear witness to it), beggars and vagrants are still there. They simply went a bit deeper underground, submerged and trying to survive, buried alive.

Among them there is a man, still young, named Thierry. He is a *zonard*, a dropout. Having lived on the streets since the age of fifteen, he is now thirty-three. "The age of Christ at his death," François says to me. It is the birth of a friendship that neither could have expected... François very quickly devises a documentary project about Thierry: filming him for a whole week, he most importantly looks at him, listens to him. Thierry says he chose long ago to live on the streets. He tells him about drugs, squats, people, but also the long journeys, backpack on and hair in the wind, most often toward the south, Spain or Biarritz, Morocco. François admires the black energy emanating from Thierry's body, its blasts of anger and its spirit of freedom.

What François does not know yet is that Thierry had already been filmed for a long period in his youth, at the very moment that he began his wanderings and in a series of programs on childhood called "Du côté des enfants." The film was made by Bernard Bouthier and is called *La Bande*, the gang.

You see there the same Thierry as a kid, and already on the streets with his little gang of friends, in the Square de la Jonquière in the northern 17th arrondissement of Paris, , "a popular spot for the selling and consumption of drugs, with some hang-out spots for young people in dire circumstances," as it is described still today in a police report.

The coincidence will reoccur a few months before his death: Thierry is filmed a final time, by chance, in the frame of a news item on Patrick Giros, a priest who takes care of street people. Thierry is a black hole, a quite exceptional gravitational force: if this simple homeless man was filmed twenty years apart by three different film crews, it is that he has a magnetic allure. As soon as he enters into the camera's vision, he breaks the cycle of images to give off an expression, a body movement, a voice.

The problem for any film is to find the money to make it.

François applies to the dynamic little company Films des Village and for a writing grant from the National Centre for Cinematography. Sometime later, he writes to me:

Old friend,

This week has been a revelation and a shock. It has ended up by convincing me to devote myself for the moment to documentaries. It is really there, believe me, that we find today the only true need for films. With each film we must feel its essentiality to its maker. For there is in "the real" such a demand for the subject that, like a categorical imperative, it imposes some fundamental questions. Where to put the camera—nothing but that—will determine the point of view, and every time a window opens onto the world. This is all that fictional filmmaking has lost today.

I leave you with my warmest embrace. Know that I think often about you.

François has made his decision, and I feel he is ready and determined. Based on the two films he has already made, the raw footage that he has filmed himself and a series of interviews with people who have met Thierry on his slow wanderings, he will weave a very subtle work, a play of echoes and resonances between the various moments in his life, and give birth to one of the most impressive documentaries of its time: *Thierry, portrait d'un absent.*

*

It is a little locket that opens. And that opens François' film.

LAURE (*Thierry's mother*): That's a little locket that was given to me. It was to hold a photo of my son. You can only use a very small photo. I cut up a photo of him so I could put it into the locket. That way, I always carry it with me. But you know it is quite hard to open, which is just as well… You could say it is a tiny photo. You can't put anything bigger in it, but it is him, it is my son.

The film begins in an almost anodyne way with this interior scene in a little, modest-looking apartment while you hear a voice. It is a thin, quavering voice, a voice through which flows, in a controlled despair, all the distress and dignity of a mother. It is a fragile voice. The final shot of the first scene shows us Laure's two hands wrapped round the locket, two hands joined as if in prayer, making a trembling shell around a baby bird.

All the terrible gentleness of the film is right there from the start in the helplessness of a mother, proud of her son *despite everything*, carrying his love, his wreckage, wrapped around her neck.

You can also read in it, discreetly and just beneath the surface, François' conception of cinema: no plaintive supplication, no grandiose appeal to the sentiments, but a simple effect of presence. No grand words or beautiful images. It is a tiny photo that opens onto an immense space, breaks into it, a vibrant presence lodged in the opening of a simple locket.

*

Thierry is a story of decay and resistance.

A man goes to the limits of his endurance. He has chosen to be on the streets, he never bows his head.

He broke out, as they would say at the time. Or rather, very quickly, he explodes, he explodes himself. Through cold, hunger, blows, drugs, his long walks through the streets. His face swells up, the child disappears.

He can "have moments of such violence that regularly, for short periods, he finds himself in prison."

He can also at times show himself to be the most horrible character. "I think it was to make sure he was loved unconditionally," says Cécile Rocca, who is today in charge of the *Collectif Les Morts de la Rue*, the Collective for the Street Dead.

From prison, however, he writes some wonderfully tender letters to her...

Prison de la Santé (A letter from Thierry read off camera)

"Letter to Cécile. I really long for the hard times on the road, and I miss Spain so much. Springtime is finally here, everything heralds it: the mildness of the air, the softer light as it gently turns the façade of the prison pink, the joyful sounds that rise up from the streets. Paris in the springtime makes even the wisest people agitated...

And then, with a great lucidity:

(the reading of the letter off camera continues)

...Too bad I have no right to it.

*

His love is also monstrous, always writing to his mother: "I kiss you all over."

LAURE (*reading a letter from her son*): "Mama, I am in Toulouse. I phoned you twice, two days ago. Are you okay? I am with a girl, we are happy together. Kisses all over. Thierry."

"We are taking shelter in the waiting room of the railway

station, as outside the mistral is there. Our hearts are still just as hot. Your son who embraces you all over."

"Mama, I love you, I am in Avignon, I think about you a lot. I embrace you all over. Your son who loves you, Thierry."

I don't know why he took to saying to me "I embrace you all over." "Your son who loves you…" I love you, too…ah… memories…

FRANÇOIS (*Off camera*): When he wrote to you like that and he finished by saying "I embrace you all over," what did you say to him yourself?

THE MOTHER: But I said to him: why are you writing "I embrace you all over"? You don't embrace your mother all over, you have never kissed me all over. –But no, Maman, that means that I love you, I embrace all of you. –Yes, but people, I told him, they don't understand. They are bound to wonder why you say that. –Ah I don't give a shit what people think, I write what I like as I love you.

Then I said to him, "Very well, my son…"

Thierry represents the complete opposite of a social world with its fixed ideas and etiquette. Against social breakdown and brainwashing, he is as mobile as he can be, in perpetual movement, has no regard for the place that people wish to assign to him. He does not even believe in the old distinction between friend and enemy. Mutual aid, forgiveness, charity… he no longer believes in anything but the hatred he sees around him, that is, in reality.

THE DIRECTOR (*Bernard Bouthier, off camera*): Do you prefer having friends or enemies?

THIERRY: Oh…enemies.

THE DIRECTOR:Why?

THIERRY: Because…with friends you know them…Friends are

just enemies, basically.
THE DIRECTOR: Would you like to live in a world where everyone helped each other?
THIERRY: No, that would be so fake!
THE DIRECTOR: Try to imagine what would be for you a world where this would be a good thing.
THIERRY: That would be too stupid, too! No matter how, that cannot exist and you shouldn't think of things like that. Because if you think them up, you go stupid! You have to take on reality, that's all. That is why I am tough, I take on reality!

*

The film is also an indictment as this homeless person, reduced to the state of a shadow, is also a luminous being who casts a harsh light on the world that surrounds us and on certain aspects that, normally, we do not want to see, or that are not shown to us.

Thierry, portrait d'un absent is not a diatribe. It does not moan. It does not complain. It does not rant and rave: it shows. It "takes on reality." It does not claim to denounce, rather contenting itself with *enouncing*. And this simple rebuke is enough to land a magisterial blow to the spinelessness of our times. A punch that hits at once the head, the stomach and the heart. Its gaze is neither scientific nor compassionate. Like a true punch, it is simply well placed.

Judges, doctors, politicians and police officers: the whole thing was a debacle. No one saw anything coming, nobody could or wanted to see, no one was concerned. Thierry is but a "drifter..." as a judge says to François. This judge saw Thierry four times, but he doesn't remember him. What about after? All the parasites of the social order hum away, naïve people are shocked, moralists trumpet. But the truth is that the France of the past forty years indulges the strongest and is pitiless toward the outsiders.

Here and there a few consciences, certain street educators, survive. Father Patrick Giros, for example. He worked a lot with the delinquents, the drifters, the prostitutes. He came into contact with Thierry several times and is a seasoned witness of the degradations of the itinerant lifestyle. Yet he does not believe his eyes: "Such an institutional and structural blindness, such gibberish from the medical authorities, such a lack of coverage in the media…" Ordained as a priest in 1968, Father Giros was at one point even tempted by the scale of the disaster to become a terrorist, before changing his mind. He founded Liberty to the Captives, a non-profit organization whose mission is to support street people. Its name comes from the Bible, a verse from the Book of Isaiah: "The Spirit of the Lord God is upon me; because the Lord hath anointed me to preach good tidings unto the meek; he hath sent me to bind up the brokenhearted, to proclaim liberty to the captives, and the opening of the prison to them that are bound…" "But," he concludes, "the city continued to produce its share of desperate young people, of lost children, without any care for them."

Thierry, portrait d'un absent is a poignant account and a perfectly judged great cry of revolt. Free from resentment and lacking any pathetic plea. Hatred is not on its side, but is on the side of the institutions, of the immense social cogwheel that crushes, that chews up, that pulverizes, that spits out. Indifference, selfishness, fatalism, apathy, resignation? Yes, no doubt there is a little of all that but it is ultimately about hatred that is mechanical, unthinking, enforced, indifferent to others and to itself. It is Thierry's cry that sounds out in the middle of the film, right in front of a lady in a blue hat who lectures him: "There it is, hatred, do you hear hatred? It is hatred that speaks!"

A quarter of a century later, the hatred is still there. It has taken on different forms, is targeted sometimes elsewhere, yet always has the same sets of targets: the weak, the undocumented or the homeless, the tramp, the drug addict, the migrant, the beggar, the refugee, the prostitute.

They are everywhere: in our streets, under our doorways, in our stairwells. They are close by and yet also terribly distant. You find them in the metro passageways or in the entrances to buildings, in stations and in squares, over air vents and under bridges.

It is the non-society: they no longer have any social role, don't even want one, and they are a nuisance. The residents complain. They are dirty, they stink. They are no longer useful or "productive," they have come off the merry-go-round, they are no longer customers, the salaried, or users. They are used up, worn out. And, as sporting metaphors seem to structure all levels of society today, understood only in professional and athletic senses: they are not, and have not qualified.

They drown themselves, they can no longer come back to the surface, they are left to drown. Some of them no longer ask anything of anyone else. They infect, they are infected. Kicked down. No one even knows how many they number: three, maybe four million. They are infinitely varied. They no longer believe in solidarity or in friendship. They don't claim any community, any identity. The residents are afraid, they look out at them from their residences. They are islands, wandering, dying, superb and isolated.

How many Thierrys are there in France today?

*

As the months pass, Thierry becomes elusive and is already no longer of this world. He travels less and less and gets high more and more. His revolt exhausts him and is no longer heard. No one can get through to him anymore, everyone gives up on him.

Thierry is a tough, even traumatic film. It has no distasteful hero-making. When you see Thierry's face at the end, his lips chapped, gnawed by drugs and swollen by alcohol, bloated by pain, and when you recall the opening scenes, the mischievous child running through the rose bushes and the black trunks of the lime trees on the Square de la Jonquière, the contrast is almost unbearable.

And then these calm sentences that come to put an end to his suffering: "Thierry died on 14 December 1991, of an alcohol, pill, and heroin overdose in this hotel room in Avignon. At dawn, he choked in his sleep. Those who were with him woke him and put him into the shower. But they then left him and let him go back to sleep. On their return, Thierry was dead, his two fists clenched, it seems, by the side of his face.

*

Thierry Percheron was buried in the cemetery of Montfauvet in the Vaucluse, close to Avignon. His grave was not far from that of Camille Claudel, who was buried in the same cemetery on 21 October 1943 after thirty years of family-instigated confinement at the psychiatric hospital close to Montdevergues. Fewer than fifty years later, Thierry was buried in plot 21. It is a plot reserved for the destitute.

Grave number 3.

Directly into the ground.

François' film, *Thierry, portrait d'un absent*, is all that remains of his time on earth.

3. JAPAN
EXERCISES IN VANISHING

In 1992, I left for Japan. I was to do my military service there for 16 months: a quarter of a century later, I am still there. In an old passageway in Paris, I was taught the classical sciences: letters, Latin, Greek, philosophy and poetry, music. Now, in a magnificent residence surrounded by the whole of the Orient, I turn toward my illustrious retreat to prepare for the future: Japanese, Chinese, calligraphy, and natural sciences. In-depth study of the cosmos, of time, of bodily and chemical systems. From time to time, nuclear physics! I take note of the great masters of the past and initiate myself into the future generations. In writing, that is the secret: mastery of your heritage and poetic innovation. A season begins.

I lost touch a little with François in the months that preceded my departure while he was wandering the streets and I was preparing myself to become the Son of the Sun. But those close to me still flew to see me. François was one of my first visitors.

I see again my house in Kyoto, in the Shimogamo district, at the very spot where the Kamo river splits in two, in the shape at once open and pointed like a Y. I live at the intersection of the two branches, below the river. All my life, you will see me at the crossroads, on the edge, at the crossing—I love nothing more than breaks and bifurcations. Here, a few steps away, stands one of the oldest sanctuaries in the archipelago: it was already there two centuries ago, before Kyoto became the capital of Japan. Out of the way, calm, protected from the chaos of tourism, it is surrounded by a forest which people say has never in its history been ravaged by fire. Yet it is never planted, pruned, or cut. It is a sacred forest: it protects the city from demons.

At the temple in the autumn, all is red: the wooden buildings, the little stone bridge, the entryway portico. Shimogamo is a red jewel in the center of the forest. The closer you get to it the more you see its different shades, the changes in tone, its reflections. The buildings are wine-colored, the bridge has crimson tints, the portico has orangey tones. But when you walk away on the gravel path that crunches beneath your feet and you turn back halfway to look at it, while your back was turned the sanctuary has become again a huge red fire that lights up the hillside and watches over the city from high up in the fiery canopy. This is where I live, in the ruby refuge at the confluence of two rivers, in the heart of the wooded hideaway.

From time to time, there is the rumbling of thunder: an archer on horseback cuts across space and shoots an arrow into the very center of a target one meter in diameter set sixty meters away. At full speed, at a gallop, without changing course at all. That is lightning. You turn your head and it has already disappeared.

My house is a few steps away. You would not be able to find it if you went by the main walkways. You have to follow the river for a few meters then, on your left, take the little path. That way, there are three or four plots of paddy fields rising gently in a row up the slope, after which the terrain bends and falls abruptly, slipping out of sight. Suddenly, there is a silent area. Smells of sawdust and green tea, perfumes of wisteria and incense. The lanterns stand out like sculptures in the sunlight, the grass trims the paving stones in green, a stony path leads to the gray terrace where, among the bamboo trees, sits my house. It appears, as if from nowhere, in the middle of the mulberry trees.

In front of my house and beyond the path is the opposite bank of the river, above which stretches out the other side of the city, where each dwelling is decorated with a bunch of bamboo or a pine branch. Finally, behind the house is a narrow, high stone staircase, where sometimes an eagle comes to sit. People often ask me why I have stayed in Japan for so long. It is because of this staircase and this eagle. If you climb the stairs at the exact spot where this eagle sits, you suddenly see things more clearly and all your perspectives are profoundly changed. In Japan, I have found my viewpoint on the world.

*

The discovery of Japan also had a profound impact on François. I see him once more as he took his first steps in the little wooden house by the river. He is shy, overawed: a Japanese house! At first, holding back in the shadows, he leans slightly and his long, curved chest emerges slowly from the paper partition behind which he stands, almost hiding. Then, he enters the straw-colored light of the room. The smell of tatami enchants him. It is the smell of a hut: the blending of rice and bulrush gives off a discreet aroma scattered with little strips of gold. Touch also: it is soft and silky when your fingers brush against them in the direction of the weaving, grainy and rough in the opposite direction. A whole palette of sensations under your fingers. You make contact once more with the ground and, how strange it is, as soon as the foot touches the straw, you breathe better. There are passageways in our bodies, forgotten tunnels, secret corridors: from the soles of our feet to the fibrils of the bronchus, from the roots of our hair to the points of our ankles.

François opens the door without making a sound and disappears into the interior on tiptoes. Light shines in and onto the wall. On the right, my old dial-up telephone, set on the table made from Camellia wood; on the left, a conical lamp leaning over a tray of red apples. Farther in, you see the half of a lampshade, a paper lamp with dashes of color. Softness, calmness: the leaves of the trees close to the window bathe the room in green glints.

Japan suits him well: a strange mix of sharp contours, of cutting gestures (making the sliding doors glide with a firm wrist, pouring without shaking boiling water into the teapot), of floating attitudes, bearings, of diluted forms (breathe in the vapors from this bowl of tea, look at the curls of steam that coil in the air and that slide out the window on a summer's evening). He is perfectly at ease in this floating world.

What François finds in Japan is this: floating. Floating against friction. Evading, the ruse, the folding screen. Thierry's death from an overdose in a hotel bedroom haunts him. He is coming away from exhausting days spent filming the wreckage of the streets, documenting social misery, taking on the full force of the immense hidden violence that accompanies the production of wealth in a so-called civilized country. He put his finger on the extraordinary, abrasive brutality of a system where injustice and clear consciences mix: day after day, night after night, he bore witness to the damage inflicted by this system, taking everything, uprooting everything, friction upon friction, and leaving behind it nothing but scraps of clothes and rags of flesh, scraps of speech, and lives reduced to the state of rubble. He saw bodies destroyed, as if they were rubbed down with sandpaper, their veins blue and bloodless for having been injected into too much, their lungs in shreds, their faces ravaged, their futures wrecked.

But in Japan, in a foreign and distant land, he rediscovers beauty and sweetness in a new light. Often, he lies flat on the tatami, extends his arms and legs and pushes his head back into the sunlight: it is as if he were swimming in a great sea of light. His very face changes: his features are broader and softer, he opens up once again, he becomes lighter. The upper part of his chest is raised once again. It is springtime, he is wearing loose-fitting clothes, white shirts, the sleeves and shoulders float, the neck is freed.

A few years earlier, Roland Barthes also came to know this extraordinary *return to grace*: as he was coming out of a slightly vain controversy with a Sorbonne professor, Raymond Picard, over a book on Racine, the director of the Franco-Japanese Institute, writer Maurice Pinguet, invited him to Japan for a few months. It is there that Barthes would find again his strength and serenity and branch off into a more personal and unclassifiable form of research, far from the commotion of the university.

In Japan, François' body sails more and more against all that is solid or dense—he holds himself in a sort of floating indeterminacy which is neither a dilution nor a disintegration. He gets rid of everything he does not need. He smiles all the time, you would say he is on his way to a state of bliss, vanishing. He is evanescent. He is fading away and coming back to life on the other side. He experiences that supreme liberty: disappearance.

In order for this phenomenon to take place, you need to know how to cut yourself off, absent yourself—to become part of the resistance or, rather, to go underground.

*

Japan is the place to go to for this kind of disappearance.

To disappear in this way is not to destroy, on the contrary. Nor is it to flee, to collapse, or disperse. It could be a loss, but it is not a deprivation. It is not (at all) a burial, (even less) a dissolution. It is instead more like a slow, controlled emptying, a distancing from unessential things, a rarefaction.

"How are you? You have become quite a stranger…" You could not have put it better. At a reception, you go by the window to smoke your cigarette and suddenly you're gone, vanished into thin air… At a cocktail party, you absent yourself: you go out for five minutes, you never come back. Here, there, farther still: you become *rarefied.* People think you are in Tokyo, you are in Peking, they call you in Peking but you are already in Taiwan. Someone thought they saw you at Saint-Germain, you were in Saint-Denis (La Réunion), then they look for you in New York, but they find you in Paris (Texas). People no longer know how to relate to you—and most often they don't suspect that you have changed places, they simply do not see you. You were there all the time. You have all of your time. Nothing arrogant or pretentious. Quite the contrary, you are modesty itself. You are becoming an expert in the art of disappearance.

Our great master in this regard is Tanizaki. In that subtle little book, deliciously titled *The Secret*, you listen to him give advice on getting to know the techniques of dematerialization. First off, Tanizaki refuses the easy way. He is not going to hide himself away in a little provincial town or in some isolated suburb. No, it is in the heart of the city that he decides to find "certain surprising little spots that are now lifeless and ignored by everyone." And not in any old city, but in the biggest in the world: Tokyo. It is here "in the bustle of the working-class areas" that he will seek to find "some peaceful oasis where only certain specific people in very specific circumstances go" ... And he adds, with an almost scientific precision, "just like how in a flash flood pools of still water are formed here and there."

To find still water in the flash flood, François and I develop, with Tanizaki, a series of erratic methods that ends up forming the outline of an unshakable strategy:

1. In your hometown (or the one you live in, your "permanent residence," as they say), every time you go out find a street where you have never set foot;
2. Always set out to find the "lower town" area in the heart

of the big city: leave the carefully planned avenues, the well set-out boulevards, and throw yourself into the inextricable maze of countless streets and alleys, convinced that "the key to disappearing lies there";
3. Refuse the *routine*, that is to say the crowded avenues and the well-trodden paths. Sometimes, all it takes is to turn off onto a crisscrossing alley to have the surprise of emerging onto a neglected and completely deserted area;
4. Walk through each town like a stowaway or secret agent; go out, especially at night: when the night falls, when the daytime workers go to bed, when the scents rise and the real town begins to breathe;
5. Find in every town its medina or *sestieri*: the exact angle where a street sketches an unforeseen angle and opens the scene up to a new meaning, where a boulevard fissures into the joyous network of secondary streets, where the detour down an alleyway transports you in to a secret spot in the blink of an eye, held in reserve outside the path of time;
6. Privilege the half-light, dive into dark places and the poorly lit passageways, get into the habit of pushing half-open gates, go inside buildings, slide yourself into the interstices, explore all the orifices, muse in *shady* areas, listen to the fault lines and the fissures, sound out the crevices;
7. Finally, everywhere, stubbornly seek out the places you have never been to.

Thus, you will find at every moment peace and quiet, and the unexpected things. You will banish the self-important and the tiresome, and you will keep by your side only your books, your loves, and your friends.

*

This werewolf life very quickly provokes a remarkable growth in all intellectual faculties, sensory as well as cognitive. Better than hashish!

We leave, we travel. We take the boat to Osaka and cross the well-named Inland Sea. It is a slow crossing without stops, and at the same time a journey to the interior of the self. Threading its way between three large islands (Honshu, Shikoku, and Kyushu), the Inland Sea is a long stretch of water fringed by a mix of verdant panoramas interspersed with devastated industrial landscapes.

François looks at the islands, set out like brushstrokes on the canvas of the sea. He observes everything, he absorbs, he takes in: he can stay for hours looking at the summit of a mountain or the hollow of a ravine. He sails from one surprise to another. Japan suits him. We have still seen only a part of it. It is the trick of the screen that folds, unfolds, and folds again... The screen never lets you see but a fragment, one moment of the landscape, playing a different part of the score back each time: "It is one of Bach's fugues," François says. "A form of composition with many parts, with a subject and counter-subjects that seem to escape at each moment, to flee and come back together incessantly from voice to voice."

In this archipelago is played out a certain logic of emergence, of appearance and disappearance that trains the eye, sharpening it to a maddening degree. It is not by chance that Japan has given to the world some of its greatest filmmakers. We watch the films of Ozu, of Kurosawa, of Mizoguchi...the holy trinity. But also, Naruse, Ichikawa, Oshima, Itami, Suzuki... *Chambara* Samurai films, *Yakuza* gangster films, porno stories and portraits of women, the golden age and new wave: our thirst to see and to know is unquenchable. In my papers I found a list of the films we saw on this trip. Far from complete, even as it stands it forms the outline of a strange poem where I find again the whole palette of that time, its *kernel*, its energy, where you read in a certain way the whole history of our life:

A Diary of Chuji's Travels
The Mother, Sleep at Mother's Breast, Youth of the Beast, Proud of my Son
The Boss's Son at College, The Boss's Son's Youthful Innocence
Standing at a Crossroads
Walk Cheerfully
Lightning, When a Woman Ascends the Stairs
Summer Clouds, Scattered Clouds, Floating Clouds, Flowing
Cruel Story of Youth, The Naked Island
At Eighteen a Girl Tells Lies, The Lady who Wept in Spring, Dexterity in Love,
The Crucified Lovers,
Branded to Kill, Pure Emotions of the Sea, The Flowers and The Angry Waves, Underworld Beauty,
Beyond the Pass, Humanity and Paper Balloons
Late Spring, Early Summer, Late Autumn, Every-Night Dreams,
Equinox Flower,
The Stories of the Last Chrysanthemums, No Regrets for Our Youth,
A Story Written With Water

François has a soft spot for Mizoguchi, *Tales of the Moon and Rain*. Why? When Mizoguchi films, it is as if he is not filming at all. Fog is fog, rain is rain, a piece of pottery is a piece of pottery. Lake Biwa suddenly appears before you or rather it *rises again* to the surface as if it were buried in you since the beginning of time. You don't see, you *smell* the reeds that brush against the boat, you follow the path alongside the river, you hear the voices of the dead carrying through the mist, you are submerged in the women's odor that floats in the night. So much so that, as André Bazin said, a quotation that François writes down in the little notebook that he bought close to the river: "The cohesion of visual, auditory, and spatial sensations creates an immense and complete provocation of the human brain."

*

But to really know Japan, you have to go to Tokyo. After the boat, the train. On the way to the capital, we pass by Mount Fuji, whose inexplicable, lofty shape dominates the landscapes of the Bay of Tokyo.

François (who has read a lot of Dazai) has calculated that the slopes of Mount Fuji converge at an angle of eighty-five degrees in the paintings of Hiroshige, and of eighty-four degrees in those of Bunchō. With Hokusai, this angle is about thirty degrees. And on a military map (he checked that too!), he notices that the angle of the east-west slopes is 124 degrees, and that of the north-south slopes is seventeen degrees. What does this mean? Why all these different measurements? On seeing Fuji, all calculations go astray. This slippage, this impossible superimposition between the numbers, the images and reality would haunt François all his life.

On his return to France, he would write me the following words: "Mount Fuji is photogenic, but something in it resists all images. The overabundance of views does not exhaust its beauty and no single view could give an exact account of the impression it produces 'in reality'."

In Japan, François discovers a simple truth, but one which

changes his life: something can leave the domain of the visible; the incalculable exists.

*

There are several ways of exploring the invisible kingdom. In Tokyo, our mania for alcohol goes on unabated. The angel of drunkenness keeps watch over us.

Tokyo is the city of bars. Berlin, London, yes. New York, of course. But Tokyo is the city of bars. In this country of continual danger and alert, always exposed to some disaster—tsunami, fire, typhoon, eruption, earthquake, flooding... (Claudel indignantly wondered why they had "placed the capital of a country over the cover of a boiler")—bars are at once retreats and refuges, dens and sanctuaries.

As François said to me, always facetious, these are places that are, so to speak, *fériés*. Places for vacation, suspension, holidays amidst the surrounding din. In the middle of the perpetual bustle of the people, coming and going to work, in the heart of all this multicolored agitation, in the mad writing of the aerials, electric wires and advertising boards that form the framework of the biggest city in the world, when the horizon turns to red in the wisdom of the evening, there are, thankfully, bars.

There are bars for all tastes and budgets. Cave-bars and dungeon-bars, taverns hidden in a library or bars nestled under a railway line. Apart from the theme bars, each one madder and more surprising than the other (the tulip-bar of Shibuya, where the seats open like petals, the Alcatraz-penitentiary bar, where a jailer-waitress takes you to your cell...), there are all those less spectacular bars, but which give Tokyo its inimitable character. At the corner of an alleyway is a discreet, indeed unfindable sign: on the wall, a row of bottles lit up from behind, shelves stacked with old records; in the shadows, the pine smell of the counter, the rubbing of the diamond on the black vinyl.

Everywhere, wherever you least expect them, tiny bars, some barely bigger than a hole in the wall: the perfect place for an escape.

There is also the particular topography of the city. As soon as you leave the large, straight avenues, it is a maze of narrow, curved alleys, a succession of villages and stalls accompanied by a delicious smell of meat grilled in soya and sprinkled with bursts of laughter.

Tokyo is the city of ruses and rivers. Few people know it, but numerous small streets follow the outlines of former rivers: the beds have been filled in but the track has been preserved in the form of a sinuous path, a windy roadway or a twisting trail. Moreover, the channels of the former city of Edo have not completely disappeared and continue to irrigate the capital. Edo was crisscrossed by narrow streets and canals, punctuated with crossroads set at right angles. Roundabouts, steep paths, trap streets, spiral staircases: in the logic of a feudal city, everything was built in order to slow the progress of possible assailants. When the city was modernized and became Tokyo, the roads were widened and the structure changed completely. But Edo subsists underneath Tokyo and the new city retains its memory. In the spaces in between this palimpsestic and paleographic memory, numerous bars have come to settle.

That is why few cities are as favorable to the "long, immense, and reasoned disordering of all the senses" that alcohol can bring about. All these streams of alleyways invite you into drunkenness. Drunkenness begins beneath your feet.

If you can drink a bit of everything in Tokyo—from the vintage wines of Bordeaux to the finest whiskies of Scotland and the delicious liquors of China—it is clear that only a deep initiation into Japanese sake, the *nihonshu*, can teach you the virtues of Japanese-style drunkenness. Apart from a few French wines and some vintage rums from across the seas, no alcohol on Earth can match sake for the richness of its poetic form and effects. This alcohol says absolutely all it wants to say, creates eternally surprising situations, radiates with unknown sensations, and is finally merriness itself.

An elixir for combat, sake is also a purifying beverage. Taiwan, Hong Kong, Korea, and China—all Asia knows that its production is of divine origin. Before, the fabrication of sake in the villages was entrusted to young virgins who chewed the rice then spat it back out, their saliva thus setting off the beginnings of fermentation. People often banally say that sake has a social function (libations being supposed to lubricate interpersonal relations), but that it above all allows you to come into contact with the divine.

This is also what is confirmed, in their own way, by the knowing and subtle ways of walking of those drunk on sake in the Tokyo night. Watch them move around delicately, furtively, stealthily. They are cats dancing or fish diving, unstable particles that change their energy levels every second, crossing space in delicious swerves and detours. Kinds of singular beings who sometimes go around in groups. Something, which cannot be reduced to the wanderings of partygoers or to the picturesque quarrels of drunkards, radiates in their night. They never harass anyone (brawls here are extremely rare), but across them unfurls a whole theory of rhythm, a consummate method of disturbance, a way of thinking by rebounds, junctions, and bifurcations. An eternal smile seems to float in the half-light on their moist lips. They are its living proof: the happiness of sake is a net that pulls you into another world.

*

François' first trip to Japan did not last very long, but it is inexhaustible and would continue to nourish his work and his thought for the rest of his life.

The last scene that I hold in my memory is from the trip we took to the Inland Sea. It is 21 March: the spring equinox, but also François' birthday. François was born at the exact point where the duration of the day is the same as that of the night, and he is very proud of it (as if he had anything to do with it). He also recalls that Johann-Sebastian Bach was born on 21 March, the same day as him! He is right: springtime is them both.

We are in the boat that is taking us from Osaka to Beppu and to celebrate this triple-event, we have bought some sake. There is a public bath in the hold: toward midnight, it is completely empty and we slip into it. In the bath, the both of us stretched out, we watch the immense sea of ferociously black oil on which float here and there a few fishermen's lights, the glow of small boats, through the big, oblong-shaped porthole. We are in the bath, we are sailing in convoy, a glass of sake in the hand. At that precise moment, we taste a perfect moment: the blue black sea in its perfect limpidity, the transparent happiness of the bath, the intoxication of the rice-based alcohol, the lapping of the water tapping away on the sides of the boat, the waterline of the ship joining up exactly with the edge of the bath, an obvious marker of this coincidence between us and the world. François is on cloud nine: he would tell me one time that apart from the birth of his daughter, this is the happiest he has ever been. There are some perfect moments in life, this was one of them.

And now? Now, François is dead.

This evening in Montmartre, I read *The Kaidoki*. It is another travel journal, of a trip from Kyoto to Kamakura along the Tōkaidō road, a few lines written in pencil in the hand of an unknown writer in which I read: "The traces of the steps I made yesterday are today a dream. Today, where I am just now, in what place will I say tomorrow that it was yesterday? In truth, the months and the years that we have left behind us, from dream have turned into dreams. Paths and mountains of yesterday and today, clouds enter the clouds."

And in these few words written at the beginning of the 13th century on a dusty road I feel rise up a faint brilliance, like a trembling or, to put it better, a *vertigo*, which is that of Japan, but also that of the past itself.

4. RUE SAMBRE-ET-MEUSE
WHAT CONNECTS US

Now I let the sentences come and open up and unfold one by one. Arriving and devouring distance, they suppress it. The times of silver and sun rise up. Time and space are dissolved: I walk in my memory, I climb back up the road and I climb back through time. Suddenly, the feeling of the irreversibility of time, unique to a nostalgic remembering, absents itself. The road is steep and, as I climb back up it, I have the feeling of taking on time from behind: to write is to pass over to the other side of it.

Reminiscence is like a glint of light that passes too quickly over a wall, a rapid luminous signal: a flash and then nothing. Sporadic appeals, desperate signals. Nothing to hold onto. Memory on the other hand is Morse Code. Short sounds, long sounds, a crackling combination, a spluttering alphabet. Thus, the dispatches can be written, the waves pass. Memory sparkles and scintillates, transmission is assured.

I have come back to the Rue Sambre-et-Meuse. Nostalgia has a formidable charm, but it is something else I have come to look for here. Events suddenly appear to go into reverse in an extraordinary way. And whereas I expected to find only the sadness, regret and melancholy that are attached so often to the phantoms of the past, I am caught up by the sounds of spring, the smell of the lilacs, the rays of sunlight that play on my hand and succeed in closing the refrigerator of nostalgia, pushing it far away. Memory is nomadic: it follows only the paths it wants to.

I pass by the post office once more from where he sent me hundreds of letters. In a corner, the past keeps watch. The restaurant Le Coin de Verre, which once sat at the intersection of the Rue Sambre-et-Meuse and the Rue Sainte-Marthe, is no longer there. But I thread my way between the days in the slip road of time, between the double harness of the past and the present. The jets of light on the balconies make my memory shimmer. I very precisely see at which angle the Place Saint-Marthe opens up, the familiar movement of the streets, the knowing signs, I hear the rumbling of the trucks and the laughter of the sidewalk: Rue du Buisson-Saint-Louis and Rue Saint-Maur, the Passage Hébrard… Again I see François walking the length of the Boulevard de la Villette, his cigarette in hand: he is disheveled, nonchalant, worldly. Open to encounters, to the light wind. These are the most beautiful times in the world, a joyous and free brightness floods the boulevard and lights up his face. We were then far away from the deceptions of time.

*

Despite its name, the district of Belleville is not an immediately beautiful place. Its very singular elegance reveals itself only to those who are not afraid, speak several languages, know how to read between the lines of the streets and the fissures of the buildings. Aragon, one of the few, and better than anyone else, knew how to pay homage to it in a description that still rings true seventy years later: "This part of Paris, with its little dilapidated stores, the sadness of its grocery store shelves, the flaking houses, ashamed by the billboards that are so old that you can no longer see them, is a pang of anguish for men who are used to the western districts, the elegant heart of the capital. It does not have the romanticism of the Marais, the historical memories of the Quartier Saint-Honoré, the lyricism of the Place des Victoires. There is nothing there to incite your dreams or imagination. Nothing here is the monument to anything. Yet some events must have happened here, in the convulsions of the city and of history, though because we remember only that which happens to the great families, these popular streets have kept nothing for our urban legends. Or if they do hold a secret, it is well hidden, totally lost. Finally, it is other people who are moved by this place." I am one of those "other people," and François was, too.

At the time I am talking about, the houses are no doubt less flaky than in Aragon's time, but the streets are dilapidated, even smashed up in several spots. The area is constantly undergoing renovation and yet never seems to look any fresher or more up to date. No record shops, no vintage boutiques, "must see" bars, organic groceries, or art galleries. No chief executive on the horizon or any designer in the neighborhood. The Rue Sambre-et-Meuse is not a *spot*, it is not *hype*, not fashionable, not *trendy*. On the other hand, the area harbors several communities that are full of surprises and the Place Sainte-Marthe is already a marvelous oasis where you can enjoy a glass of white wine as you tilt your head back into the sunlight.

The population is varied, as Belleville knows how to be. There are the Kabyles and the Tunisian Jews, also the Chinese from Wenzhou, a city south of Shanghai that provides, with a few people from Qingtian, the battalions of workers for the hidden workshops. More and more Turks, Africans, Sri Lankans and

Malays, multicolored populations that come together only at the Parc de Belleville or the supermarket. But already their children go to school together and, based on this mosaic of memory, create new forms of identity.

A whole parallel economy is developing behind the mean-looking walls and shutters of gray metal that never open up to prying eyes: money games, Macao-style gambling dens, illegal medical surgeries… Above all, the "little dilapidated stores" have given way to a swarm of illegal clothing workshops that are just as shabby but are almost completely invisible. From time to time a van stops, filled with bags of fabric or with bundles of cloth, loads or unloads and leaves again at high speed—the slamming of doors, a vague smell of sheep or buckskin floats over the sidewalk and it is already over. The police may well raid the place now and then, but the tiny shops packed with shady workers and sewing machines start back up again almost instantly, working night and day in a racket of bobbing needles and multicolored pieces of cloth.

François is immediately very at ease in this underground, ever recreating world: he delights in the creaking of the pedals and the clicking of the needles coming from the back yards as if an organism of muscles and metal, of tendons and cables, hidden away behind the walls, was knitting in the shadows an immense mechanical symphony, decorated with a few rags of cloth and scraps of human skin. He likes this area with its mix—typically Belleville—of large modern buildings, little French bistros and Chinese restaurants. When night comes, we can go and eat a Peking duck on Mandarin crêpes, spicy pork with caramel or coriander fried shrimps. On the table there are always green vegetables with long leaves and in the air floats an odor of washed cucumbers and sesame seeds.

*

On 17 November 1993 the film *Libera me* by Alain Cavalier was released in cinemas. The filmmaker won the Prix du Jury at Cannes for his preceding film, *Thérèse* (as well as six Cesars, including best film, best director, and best screenplay), but his new work greatly perplexed many critics.

Filmed solely in close-ups and semi close-ups, *Libera me* is a film without speech or music, and almost without a story: there is certainly a succession of tableaux where you can guess a storyline—fathers, sons, prisoners and guards, executions, coded signals, clandestine messages—but it is all done in the total absence of sets, dialogues and narration. For this paradoxical essay written in a radically new cinematographic language, Cavalier chose a 27 year old rookie assistant director: François.

Screened in Cannes, *Libera me* is in turns applauded and booed. For some, it is a "rare object," an "impressionist painting," a "maximalist work," or "tragic blueprint." For others, it is an exercise in "mortification" by a "paranoid author," which provokes "a sentiment of solitude and abandon." This "film of the in-between time, new and virginal," immediately incites admiration or exasperation. As only Cavalier could!

Libera me is clearly a difficult filmic object to classify. The plot is strange, indeed inexplicable. When Cavalier comments on a few images from the film in his immediately recognizable way, dry and clear and with no frills, the trouble is doubled: "Teenagers have kidnapped a police officer in a café. They coat him in Mercurochrome, they release him. A warning? Invention of a form of struggle other than murder? Black humor and derision? What do they want?" Yes, it is true: what do they want? Excellent question!

Add to all that the title taken from the Catholic liturgy,

in Latin, and you will have an idea of the perturbation it provoked. *Libera me* is the prayer that closes the funeral ceremony at church and asks for complete deliverance from sin: *Libera me, Domine, de morte aeterna*... "Deliver me, Lord, from eternal death..." What, a title in Latin? One imagines today the cries of the filmmaking franchises. But you must be dreaming? Yes, true cinema is a dream awakened.

One cannot however help being struck by the beauty of the lighting, the elegance and the rigor of the editing, the precision of the shots. Static shot, tight frame: here is the closed fist of a young man, his wrist wrapped with the handkerchief of his loved one. It is the police officer who has allowed the prisoner to keep his talisman. And there, some baked apples recall Cézanne's oranges: they *ring out* on screen like a declaration of love and, as Cavalier himself says: "These images can also have other meanings, the viewer will find them without difficulty according to the path their life has taken." Do you see? Do you understand?

A final heresy: three years of work and three months of editing, *Libera me* is also a *thrifty* film (it cost less than five million francs at the time, when the average was twenty-three million), filmed in budgetary conditions of great lucidity: "Money is the enemy of the film, money is worried, concerned, it pursues the filmmaker and wants to stop him doing things." Try saying that to a filmmaker today!

François was greatly influenced by his work with Alain Cavalier. What connects François to Cavalier is at once very simple and very profound: the refusal of verbosity (of both language and image), of straightforward symbolism, the importance of non-professional interpreters (among whom François himself slides, and who give the film a sort of native innocence), the taste for detail, the density of bodies, objects, and gestures (the somber secret of a skin, the brightness of a fabric), the resistance to the superfluous, all that makes of cinema a hymn to the most concrete and the most profound, and the least affected, physical reality. François will show how all of this stayed with him in each of his films, beginning with *Thierry, portrait d'un absent*: "As soon as a shot has not been constructed by a filmmaker, it teaches about life today, and is instructive about cinema." *Duly noted.*

*

A room in town. François' apartment is on the third floor of number 29 Rue Sambre-et Meuse: a red carpet, white walls, but above all an appalling mess. Here it is, as described to me by François in a letter:

In the middle of an absolute shambles, on a table strewn with all kinds of papers, newspapers, garbage, empty cigarette packets, overflowing ashtrays, dog-eared books yellowed by smoke, in a room which seems to have been hit by a gas explosion or ransacked by vandals.

And it is true, there is electricity in this room. On the table, on the bed, in the closet, piles of records and mountains of books, papers everywhere, and musical scores spread around. In a corner, stacks of CDs that play on a loop all night and all day. In another, film magazines and academic journals, history books, maps of the skies and the earth… In another still, treatises on quantum physics and chemistry.

On the other side, lying on the red carpet, all sorts of dictionaries (the *Littré*, the *Larousse*, the *Gaffiot*…) that François consults constantly, gripped by an insatiable curiosity. All this creates across the apartment whole turrets of books, domes, bulbs, rotundas… a mobile architecture of varied volumes, of the geostrategic atlas in a spiral notebook. It is a small space, but it is transformed through the incredible heaping up of records, books, journals and ashtrays into a gigantic musical ship filled with smoke, ready for any crossing. The room in the Rue Sambre-et-Meuse is a worksite on which circulates all the knowledge of the world.

*

The trip to Japan stays in François' memory, he speaks to me about it often. After the filming of *Thierry, portrait d'un absent* and *Libera me*, he has only one idea in his head: to leave again. The Rue Sambre-et-Meuse becomes a base camp where François dreams of and prepares at once his films, his readings and his travels. He who has hardly ever left France before except for a brief trip to Venice which he loved, and a language-learning trip to the United States where he spent all of his time reading Proust's *In Search of Lost Time* and listening to the entirety of Bach's cantatas, is suddenly gripped by the desire to leave. He is, as he writes in a lovely phrase, "homesick for every country":

What would I give to be with you at this time!... In working on Paul Morand, I realize that he spent nearly ten years traveling the world for his own pleasure. Since Japan, I have been gripped by this desire to travel. I am homesick for every country.

The timing is right: *Thierry, portrait d'un absent* has just received the prestigious Louis-Marcorelles prize at the Festival du cinéma réel. As a result, he has a little money, but more importantly he has been commissioned for a film, a documentary on Tarzan. That is his chance to go to the United States for a week to meet with the American author Philip José Farmer, who has written two books on the Lord of the Jungle. After his wanderings with the street people and his initiation to Japan, it is a striking contrast, but he accepts. It gives him the chance to travel.

*

The trip to the United States is a complete fiasco, trying but instructive. François talks about it with that humor that he keeps for the most difficult of circumstances:

Paris-Washington-Chicago-Louisville-Chicago-Los Angeles-Chicago-Peoria (Illinois)-Chicago-Paris. That was our itinerary! A week where I spent most of my time in airports, in midair, on roads, and in the infamous "Motel 6s" that you only get in America. These daily changes in time zones and climate ended up—with the help of fatigue—sending me into a trance, like in hypnosis. A hurricane or a sandstorm could have started up and I would not have been in the least surprised.

There are also a few moments of wonder, for example on the way into Los Angeles: "Los Angeles seen from the plane is something I won't forget in a hurry. For the final hour, you fly over the great Nevada Desert, you cross the Rocky Mountains covered in snow and then dive over L.A., which stretches out across the whole valley as far as the eye can see and is stopped in the west only by the ocean. The city is flat, cut into straight lines, and at night, millions of lights make it look like the structure of a gigantic spaceship ready to take flight. All of this little world moves around furiously and gives the impression of running joyously into the Apocalypse."

But more generally the trip to the United States did not bring to François his wished-for feeling of discovery. He was wanting a new departure, even a lift-off, and he finds himself shuttling between motels and air terminals. The rest of the time he walks around, wanders, without meeting anyone, without any sense of engagement or triggering something new, as he puts it:

In Chicago, I tried to walk a little through the streets and reached Lake Michigan, whose banks were already frozen. But I was so numb with cold and the highest buildings gave me vertigo. So I quickly took refuge in a cozy middle-class bar where four middle-aged women, looking to rekindle the fires one more time, were very aroused by the sight of a "Frenchie." The kind of female dragons that wear the trousers and terrorize their husbands. One of them said to me in French, "Monsieur, if you don't mind, screw me right away!" I left immediately, preferring to face the cold than their flames... Besides, certain States in the Union declare unconstitutional and criminal certain "deviant" practices, namely: fellatio and sodomy. I therefore remained coy, without which the coitus could have gone wrong! I did not want to end up in prison!

The American dream would not end in Hollywood or in prison, but with an unpretentious little film that appeared under the title, quite funny when you know the circumstances, of *Moi, Tarzan*—Me, Tarzan. As for François-Tarzan, he left the United States as quickly as he could to recharge his batteries in the only jungle worth the trouble, that of Belleville, Rue Sambre-et-Meuse.

*

François is not unduly discouraged by his short American experience. In fact, he has already been working for a few months on another project, which is very dear to him.

He reads voraciously, even more than normal. Apollinaire

for example, from whom he copies these lines in a letter to me:

I am thirsty cities of France, Europe and the world
Come all and flow into my deep throat

When I pass through Paris, I stay in his ramshackle place on the Rue Sambre-et-Meuse and we look at the stars and have long talks.

There is only one window overlooking the street in the Rue Sambre-et-Meuse apartment. François perches himself there, as is his wont, for whole days and nights. By day, he observes the ballet of Chinese, black Africans and Kabyles. By night, he contemplates the stars while he unrolls endless coils of smoke into the air. If he likes the Orion constellation so much, he says to me one night as he points his finger to the three points aligned in the sky, it is that, close to the celestial equator, "it is visible from both hemispheres." He stays for a long time at the edge of the abyss: he stares at the moon, he examines the stars, the night, high above us. He wants to rediscover the secret of great communications and great combustions.

He is ready for Africa.

*

Where am I? At the end of the world. What I am doing? Nothing. Torpor is in the air and in my head, too. A few bursts of activity now and then. Barely.

From where I am writing to you to the next village, it is three kilometers. No electricity. And in the evening, after having dined there, I return to the camp to go to bed by the light of a storm lantern and the moon that has now been in the sky for two nights.

I don't know if I will return one day, but do not worry about me. Sending you all my best.

The colored postcard represents a photo of an African woman in a pink bubu as she grinds some millet. It is mailed from Rufisque, Senegal, on the 20th May 1997. It is a regular-sized card with indented edging. Through the woman's low neckline is visible the curve of a breast.

For me, this card summarizes François' African experience: at once uncertain and joyful, vaguely unsettling, lost and enchanted. In Africa, everything went very quickly, very far, and very intensely.

In 1995, François set out for Senegal for the first time. In a few months there, he set up some very deep, passionate relationships. In Dakar, in Rufisque, in Thiès, in Diourbel, in Touba, François finally rediscovers the sense of disorientation that he had experienced for the first time in Japan but in a quicker, more consistent, and more radical form. Senegal for him is first and foremost a climate, an ambiance, that he describes to me in one of his first letters:

At the beach. Full of people on summer Sundays. Nothing like our beaches or our tourists. Here, no one lies down, no one sunbathes. The beach is occupied vertically, surveyed by a compact crowd. A Champs-Elysées of sand that you climb up and come back down. Here they prepare tea in a hole sheltered from the wind, there they wrestle Senegalese-style, their bodies covered over in sand. Shouts and bursts of voices mix in with the sound of the sea, with the dense flow of the sea.

There are also movements and sounds which will mark François for life like the passage of cars in their polyphonic tumult: "The groaning sound of the Doppler radar, the clanking of unscrewed bolts, the tom-tom of shaky roofs, the whistling of torn rubber." François is literally *shaken up* by Senegal.

As expected, a woman soon arrives. A young woman with a way of holding herself. Her gaze is "haughty, slightly contemptuous." It is a look that is accustomed to flat immense spaces, that sees afar. A woman and a bearing, too. A curve: "Perhaps the small of her back is the heritage of those walks repeated from generation to generation in long caravan lines across the sandy lands..." François is crazy about her. He says it himself, he "raves." Love, death, sex, money, everything strikes him straight in the solar plexus and rushes through his body. Very quickly, the whole world will revolve around this figure and from then on his heart beats only around this fault line. So, the dice are thrown, the spell is cast, *liggéey xelam*, the horses run free. The whole universe is subject to this step full of nobility, to this neck that is elegant and provocative at the same time: "The world stalls at the sight of her. I have been gravitating around 'that' for months. A blind spot which consumes me completely."

Last letter from Africa, after the rupture, very beautiful, almost serene, with this sense of calm that can arise only in the aftermath of a great disaster:

A face and a figure come back to me, but the details are blurred. Refined, elegant, light, supple. A tone of voice, too, clear, clicking, rolling, beating. Perhaps I dreamed her up. In voicing this hypothesis, my throat knots up. But how could I doubt the power of persuasion of dreams?

It seems to me she was very beautiful. It is over.

I think I am coming back from Africa.

*

Senegal was very important in François' life. He takes from it some wounds and a vision of the world and human relationships that is both more fragile and at the same time sharper. He frees himself there, painfully and with difficulty, from a certain tendency to see the world solely from his white European and relatively privileged point of view. Inspired by the trip, he makes two films, *Facteur Toubab* and *Vacances au Sénégal*, that make a diptych revealing his doubts, his misadventures, but also his altruism and his openness.

For several years, François would be a linkman between France and Senegal: for our friend Yelli, a big and strapping guy, an illegal worker in Italy; for his sister Sarah; for his wife Edmée back home; for all the Gningue family. He travels and composes for them some "filmed letters" which circulate between the Po Valley and the Atlantic Ocean. The project, initially entitled "*What connects me*," aims to give filmed news to both sides, thus tightening the bonds loosened by geographical distancing, but also by the disjunction in ways of living, that slow isolation without return that all exiles know. He writes: "Behind the camera, I witness this many-faced separation. I am a messenger who tries to fill this space and am becoming aware of getting close to what seems to me essential in the act of filming: reconnecting that which is separated."

François grew up in 1980s France. A France that, more and more, leaned toward nationalism and xenophobia: for all of his youth, he saw the far right gnaw away at the fabric of France. He was twenty when the Front National, thanks to the introduction of proportional representation, arrived en masse on the benches of the National Assembly (with thirty-four seats) and began to spread again the myth of a "country of the white race," where to see a black television newsreader reading the evening news was still very unusual. He is the exact contemporary of the retreat from pluralism in the collective republican memory, even though France was one of the very first countries in the world to have known immigration and was able, perhaps better than any other, to take advantage of it. With Senegal, and through a practice that comes not only from the domain of knowledge but also from a strong personal experience, he finally finds the means of escaping from a certain way of thinking, still in force today, which centers uniquely on the Hexagon while disposing of—or ignoring—the plural history of France against the lie of a constitutive homogeneity.

Toward the end of *Facteur Toubab*, he has this magnificent declaration, at once so French and so Senegalese, an apology for freedom and solidarity forever entwined: "Nothing more holds me back. All that I have left is the strength of the bonds I have made here and which nothing can tear apart."

PART THREE: BREAKING THE WAVES

1. BAHIA

The next three years were good times for François. After the hard but instructive experience in Africa, he arrives in the 21st century with his head held high and his eyes fixed on the skies. The solar eclipse of 11 August 1999 is the last big European event of the 20th century. François knows it, he who has always had his head in the stars.

"A total eclipse of the sun! You know it's happening? (I know it's happening as he has been going on about it for two years). This will be the last of the 20th century... And the last, even, of the millennium!"

François is fired up, François is catching fire, François is at fever pitch. We can't miss this!

"It will be very short, a quarter of an hour in total across the whole of France. We need to prepare... The next will be in 2081, it is now or never."

The birth of the Euro? The Davos Summit? The G7 Meeting? Mere trifles. Sideshows, irrelevant. Just frothy things, of secondary importance... The great cosmic cycle: that's where the adventure is! He was barely moved by the death of Stanley Kubrick a few months earlier, even though he was one of his favorite filmmakers... François has always had his sense of priorities, and therefore a sense of nature. On the galaxies, he is a fount of knowledge. From his room on the Rue Sambre-et-Meuse, perched by the window, a book in one hand and a cigarette in the other, he invokes all the Greeks of all the ages:

"There is a total eclipse of the sun in *The Odyssey* at a key moment, when Ulysses is back in Ithaca. There is a bit of everything in Homer: winds, thunder, lightning, and earthquakes… But the eclipse is special: it always announces something. Some say it is harmful, I think it is beneficial. In *The Odyssey*, it is the revenge of Ulysses and the massacre of the courtiers. In Herodotus, it is a positive sign: a total eclipse of the sun takes place during the war of the Lydians and the Medes. When the two enemy peoples see the day transform into night they think that the gods are calling for the end of the conflict: they stop fighting and make peace!"

François prepares for the great eclipse with an admirable attention to detail. He studies the trajectory announced by the scientists, analyzes the landscape to find the best possible viewing spot and watches the weather forecasts.

"The Greeks had an amazing concept of time: *kairos*. *Kairos* is the moment, the instant T. Or rather the instant I: the instant of the instant, the instant where the instant instantaneously becomes instant. The point, the minute, the second! The comma between two phrases, the second!"

He thinks of everything, he plans, he sets things up. We rent a car several months in advance and find a clearing around Compiègne, an open space where you can set up a telescope and stretch out on the grass to look at the night as it passes.

"We need to think about getting some good glasses. Regular sunglasses are not enough. Eyes wide open! If the visibility is good, if *Kairos* is with us, the sun will go black, and at that moment we will see everything. Everything will be lit up in black. The sun should be framed by two stars: Mercury and Venus. Another positive sign: travel and love!"

Very early on the morning of 11 August, en route for the clearing to the north of Compiègne which we visited twice in the preceding months, once on the map of the National Institute for Geographical and Forestry Information bought for the occasion and a second time by car during a scouting weekend. François turns on the radio. The first item sets him at ease: the weather services indicate optimal conditions at this precise spot in the French territory, a lot more favorable than in other regions. We are in one of the best places in France for the eclipse and have prepared well.

A stop on the verge of a beautiful country road, fringed with a majestic forest area: beeches, yews, sessile oaks, lime trees with little heart-shaped, finely toothed leaves, hornbeams, and chestnut trees. We follow a shaded path for a few minutes that opens onto the little round clearing in the shape of a crown, an almost perfect circle.

François has put on his protective glasses, but I sense he is worried. There are in fact many clouds overhead. They have been building up since the morning. The wind sometimes disperses them but they come back thicker each time. François sniffs, gets up, lights a new cigarette, checks the focusing of the telescope (frowns then raises his eyebrows) and lies down by my side, barely reassured. Shadows run in bands across the ground.

The eclipse is a caravan of the night, a very narrow band of darkness: it is only a hundred kilometers wide and is to pass over France at high speed in less than a quarter of an hour. The speed of the shadow… We wait for it.

A miracle: a little before midday, the cloudy covering tears open, the conditions become ideal, I see François less and less anxious, calmer and calmer. Suddenly, it is the eclipse. It comes in a strange mix of speed and density, a black ball rolling forward the moment it disappears: that is the eclipse. *In the instant*, a great feeling of peace over the Earth. The light fades, the animals think it is night, they lie down to rest on the prairie. The temperature falls, a cool wind rises up in the heart of the summer. The birds, suddenly very calm, stop singing. Total disappearance of the disc. Perfect silence. We no longer breathe. The sun covers over in an inky black and becomes a black pearl. Then, one by one, the stars appear like golden studs stuck into the curtain of this sudden night, as precarious as it is precious, impromptu.

And, as François had predicted, Venus is visible alongside the sun. We don't know it yet, but it is a happy omen.

*

The same year, in fact, another miracle came along: this one is called Sylvia. They met a few months before the eclipse. François was thirty-three, as was she, and it is the perfect match. They become part of each other, they enchant each other, they dazzle each other. A coming together of times, humors, hopes, desire: the two stars converge, their union is like an obvious fact that asserts itself very simply. They get married quickly. Jérôme and I are the witnesses at François' wedding: we put on our best clothes and sign the register with a proud hand.

The celebration takes place on 15 September 2001, on a Parisian boat. We had visited numerous venues with François: town house (too dear), hunting lodge (too war-like), top floor of a hotel (too snobby), disused provincial chateau (too far), contemporary art gallery (too trendy)… The final choice was for a boat, moored opposite the National Library. On board!

Polka through the night. Under the yellowy light, clear silhouettes, shadowy silhouettes. The clouds stretch out in the purple sky and, on the banks of the Seine, people pass by in the shadows, alongside the poplar trees. We slip our moorings… The music sparkles, we eat a shoulder of lamb cooked in thyme, the wine flows and some even whisper that they have seen a few joints of the famous Black Pearl back from Afghanistan passed round.

*

But this is not all. When it takes off like that, love is irresistible. A little more than a year later, a third miracle. A new star appears. It has the name of a Brazilian state, of a joyous carnival, and of an album by John Coltrane: Bahia.

You could describe love, the real kind, as a freeze frame. That is to say, literally, that the film freezes. "*Faire tout un cinéma*," as they say, to make a big to-do: the film of appearances, the great circus of social relations, the comedy of human relationships. The fable of genealogies and belongings, the big screen of good sentiments, the soundtrack of chatter and patter, the clichéd video clip of professional success. And just as much: the frenetic short film of pornographic adventures, the boring full-length films of marriages of convenience, the fantastical drama of adulterous intrigues, the road movie of casual sexual relations, the B-movie of existential crises, the Z-movie of emotional dependency, the disaster movie of possessive jealousies, the horror film of domestic violence, the melodrama of family ties, all of that covered day and night by the systematic spy movie of social media. In short, the right-thinking blockbuster of rules and laws (staged cohabitation, Oscar-winning living together), the show's script in all its horror: a simplistic and authorized system of writing, obligatory and *priced*.

Love: a sudden clearing, a piercing, a breaking free. The system flees over the edges, empties itself in its center, crumbles at its sides. Its devastating tsunami, perfectly organized, rips open onto free, uncontrolled instants, simple and perfect gestures—giving, receiving, exchanging a kiss. The story of love is unclassifiable in the great catalogue of emotional relationships precisely because it is not a film. It is a novel. It does not fit into the frame; it needs the infinity of pages to unfold itself.

*

I remember Bahia.

Bahia, the daughter of Sylvia and François, was born 20 November 2002. She looks like her father, but also like her mother. Above all, she looks like Bahia.

The State of Bahia is named after the Bay of All Saints in Brazil: after the Bay of Bengal, it is the largest bay in the world. The little body that surged out of its mother's womb and finds itself right away wrapped up in blankets seems to have risen to the surface of that immense volume of water and to have taken with her the smile of a mermaid. Bahia is a bay, an indentation in the fabric of the days: she illuminates and transforms all around her. She is at first a little creek, shy, curved, closed off. Then, little by little, she is transformed into a cove, a gulf: she grows, she deepens quickly. One day, she will herself flow to the seas.

Her hair is fine and light, almost blond with golden streaks. She has two bright chestnuts for eyes. Her face is finely shaped with a very pure coloring. Her skin is pale like crystal with a few traces of red. Her mouth is exquisite, the color of cherry. Her smile is sharp, almost acidic, but her gaze is very soft, as if a flower or a sweet was always about to come out of this child.

Bahia can be patient and impatient, she is always friendly. Reserved and at the same time audacious. She takes her time, can take an hour to put her shoes on, never walks quickly, does forward rolls in slow motion on the golden sands of the Île de Ré.

At the same time, Bahia is bold and daring. She tries everything and applies herself to do well with an almost furious pride. Dance, piano, bicycles: all that requires balance and grace interests her. She will fall a hundred times from her bike, but she gets back in the saddle. She sticks to it. She will get there.

This appetite for life is also a thirst for knowledge. Bahia wants to see everything, know everything. When you make something, she comes to see. You can be cooking, hammering in a nail, cutting a rosebush, reading a book, or even simply taking a rest; she always comes to observe you.

Bahia is curious, devouring. When she asks a question, you have to reply to her. And she does not ask only one question, but a whole series of them. She is a cannon of queries, an artillery of question marks. If you don't reply to her quickly and precisely, she moves to the second phase: invasion of your personal space, quarrels, charming threats, reminders, investigations… she does all of this as she frowns like her father, making her look so sweet. When she stops talking, her eyes fix on you and no longer move, awaiting the response as she bites gently on her lip.

*

Bahia is a bay, a stretch of sea almost completely surrounded by pieces of land: her father, her mother, her friends, the "grown-ups." But she is also a shelter for her parents. This "complete beauty who would have made Petrarch sing and brought Dante to his knees," as François says with his innate sense of moderation (and of modesty), deserves a complete love. She had it.

I remember two scenes that took place a few years apart and on different continents, but which echo each other. These are very simple, very *profound* scenes. In the first, there is a bed plunged in darkness. It must be in the apartment of the villa Albert-Robida near the Buttes-Chaumont where François and Sylvia have moved to in order to have space in which to raise their child. Bahia must be three years old; she is sleeping deeply. François is watching her from the doorway. I observe him, unseen. The window is open, a cool summer breeze rushes in and flutters the curtains. Bahia is in her night clothes, the sheet thrown off. François enters, heads toward the window and catches the shutters, which he closes carefully, without a sound. He then turns toward his daughter. Going forward, he leans over to move the sheet on which Bahia is sleeping. She sleeps deeply but, as if she can hear him, he whispers: "How much I love you, my sweet." Then he kisses her.

The other scene takes place in Tokyo during his second trip there. François is sleeping in the house, in the room upstairs, on the tatamis. I go upstairs to give him a bottle of water and I see him between the sliding partitions, which are not closed properly. He has taken with him a little metal locket in which is inserted a photo of Bahia. His hands are holding the frame to his mouth and he kisses it gently. Then, after having looked at the photo for a final time, he closes over the locket and puts it back into his suitcase. But before closing the case, once the locket is in place, he brushes tenderly its edges. A magnetic current, a very soft electricity crosses the room: it is a very simple and beautiful gesture. A *charged* moment.

*

To die at eleven years old. Bahia has left in her wake swirls of tender impressions and an almost unspeakable pain. It is as if everything has been burnt with a red-hot iron then become black, burnt, reduced to ashes.

After her death, Jérôme and Isabelle would plant a liquidambar tree for her in the yard at their house in Chambon-sur-Lignon: "Because it would take a beautiful rare tree to remember this little girl who knew already how to have fun with complicated words."

The liquidambar is a tree of the Hamamelidaceae family, which originates in China. It is a dense tree, grows very straight and can reach great heights. Its fruits are brown capsules, its flowers large green and yellow pods. Its wood is the color of satin. Its leaves are palmately and give off a strong resin smell. Resin is used to treat abscesses and burns, to relieve dental pain, and to improve blood circulation. It is also used as a scent for soaps, but it is above all a balm used on wounds. The Chinese employ the leaves and the roots against cancer, the bark for skin conditions and the fruits in the treatment of arthritis and lumbago.

Each time I see one of these trees on my trips in the Szechuan province or in Taiwan, I immediately think of Bahia, then of Sylvia, the survivor, and I say a silent prayer to the great liquidambar. I have faith. It is a very resilient tree. A Chinese friend tells me that it is one of the first species to reappear after forest fires.

2. QUARREL

François has produced many documentaries since he left film school: eight in total. He dreams now of a more ambitious work, a full-length fiction film.

There is in Japan a house where artists can put their bags down for a few months and dedicate themselves to their art in the most tranquil way possible. It is found at the end of a road that winds round a mountainside amongst groves of dwarf bamboo at the heart of one of the most beautiful cities in the world, Kyoto. The Villa Kujoyama functions on the model of the Villa Medici in Rome and the Casa de Velázquez in Madrid; it is the only French artistic residence in Asia. The ideal spot for the project that we had thought up together.

Working together. Since the years of our youth at the Lycée Lakanal, this project had crossed both François' and my minds several times. Twenty years later, this project looked more and more likely to happen. It was full of promise. But life is strange and never goes quite where you want it to. This collaboration was a complete disaster and the only scar, a deep and lasting one, in our friendship.

*

The project, which will be called successively *Schrödinger's Cat*, *Uehara's Cat* and, finally, *In the Cat's Eye*, is quite simple. In my papers I found the synopsis that we had written together:

Our hero is called Albert. He is a promising young French scientist, a theoretical physicist. He is invited to Japan to participate in highly important research at Super-Kamiokande. It is here that at the end of the 20th century, Professor Koshiba's team succeeded in detecting neutrinos (elementary particles whose composition is not known) and calculating their mass, which was until then considered nil. This work won him the Nobel Prize for Physics in 2002. But the results suggest some theoretical modifications of the "standard model," the description of the fundamental laws of the universe. With other theorists from around the world, Albert is going to use the research center data. From their reflections might emerge a better understanding of the laws governing the universe and perhaps even a more precise vision of its future. Is it going to expand and cool indefinitely or, on the contrary, end up retracting?

But an event will seriously disrupt Albert's work. Until then completely absorbed by his research, he gets lost during a walk in the streets of Tokyo and falls instantly in love with an unknown woman he meets in the moving walkways of the Ebisu district. Accompanied by a black cat who takes malicious pleasure in coming to purr over his equations, he decides to go and find her and his trip goes off in a completely new direction…

Finally, Albert will discover the truth about the young woman during a journey to the north. Time has passed. It is winter. To deliver the results of his research, Albert must go for the first time to the Super-Kamiokande site. He has not found the mysterious figure and his trip is ending. He felt he was close to his goal many times, but like these elementary particles defying the laws of localization, she has always slipped away. The severity of the landscapes and weather makes this trip across the snows a real odyssey. At the end of a journey full of pitfalls and encounters, Albert glimpses the link between his amorous quest, his physical voyage, and his theoretical research. Is he about to attain that "unique lasting presence in which disappears the distinction between meaning and the absence of meaning?"

*

As can be seen, the project that we had prepared is based on three guiding lines. A place that is extraordinary and unknown: the Super-Kamiokande research center. A discipline, difficult but fascinating: particle physics. And a sentiment that, as we know, has never known any laws: love.

I found the Super-Kamiokande site during a winter journey to the Gifu region in the center of the largest island in Japan, and I spoke about it to François straight away. Situated two hundred kilometers to the north of Tokyo in a mountainous region that is often covered in snow, this research center is a stunning place: a thousand meters underground, a disused mine has been transformed into a vast cylindrical cavity in which has been installed a reservoir filled with fifty thousand tons of pure water, lined with ten thousand photoelectron multiplier tubes which look like spherical mirrors, and which track the disintegration of the proton.

It is a place of unreal beauty. Imagine a cylinder forty meters high and forty meters wide, filled with pure water. Pure water is water that has never entered into contact with another substance. Neither bacteria nor minerals: just the pure formula of water, H20. Hardly ever existing in nature, it is most often produced through distillation or a system of reverse osmosis that lets only water molecules through. The most essential nutrient for life, unaltered and unpolluted it is faintly blue and is so transparent that its color is perceptible only through several meters of thickness. All around this great bluish reservoir, the photomultiplier tubes are attached to the walls like shellfish on a rock and the ceiling lights give them a beautiful golden color through which pass sometimes fawn-colored glints. People speak in low voices and you hear noises of ablution and the droning of voices. In the middle of this pond scattered with sensors tuned in to the whole universe the scientists and the workers get around on boats by paddling like prehistoric fishermen.

Japan also interests us because it allows us to introduce an *off-center* point of view. Very often, discourse on science—and the philosophical questions that it raises or embodies—emanates in effect from Western authors imbued, suffice to say, with the founding values and stories of Judeo-Christian civilization. It is particularly blatant when science meets with the great metaphysical questions. The *Fiat lux* and the Big Bang, for example, have an undeniable connection. They both speak freely of the "genesis" of the universe, the explosion of initial "light," etc. But what about a Chinese, Arab, Syrian, or Japanese physicist? How do they relate to the epistemological debates that animate Western scientists? To want to tell this story from Japan is to *knowingly* displace the point of view, to make a less familiar and perhaps more acute voice heard, and to play at once on the confrontations and connections between cultures. On contact with the Japanese physicists, the protagonist discovers another relationship with science, the questions it engenders and that go beyond it.

As for the third axis of the project, love—but which, at the same time, is the pivotal point—it is represented by this barely-seen feminine character: the unknown beauty. As we know, in mathematics the unknown is the variable to be determined in order to find the solution to a problem. Another continent to explore!

"In the new science, everything comes in its turn, such is its excellence." Phantom particles, encounters, random displacements... In April 2005, the project *In the Cat's Eye* was chosen for the Villa Kujoyama.

*

Yet though this second trip by François to Japan began in the most promising ways, nothing would go as planned. Very quickly, convictions and certainties crumble, then fall.

How does a quarrel manifest itself? It could be a word, a gesture, a glance. Sometimes, a silence. It is an undetectable crack, coming from nowhere but spreading everywhere. At the same time, there is a profound logic to the quarrel. Each one commits himself to a path where the other does not want to or cannot go.

It is strange, the partition that separates friends during a quarrel: an impalpable and resilient window, everything smashes to pieces against this glass. Slowly but surely, this window separates us, it *warps* relations, distorts behaviors, poisons the emotions.

The quarrel. As its French name, *brouille*, suggests, it is a fog, a confusion, a thick cloud. An imperceptible mass of anodyne and isolated details which end up regrouping and even coagulating. And then, one fine morning, the unimaginable happens.

A question arrives, posed by everyone but to which no one really has an answer, for if you knew how to reply to it, the quarrel would not have taken place: what happened?

*

François' second trip to Japan is the exact opposite of the first. The first had been a miracle, a sort of floating, suspended parenthesis in the gentle softness of springtime and the perfume of the cherry trees. The second quickly becomes a hell in the sweaty furnace of summer, amidst the monkeys and the wild boars.

In fact, I have never understood what went on in his head at that time. The only thing I can do is to try to piece it together, based on his own words and how things happened. Alone in Kyoto, separated from his family and his everyday environment, it is as if he could not find his place amidst the chaos of sensations, reflections, observations and impulses that the surrounding world and his imagination incited in him. Japan escapes him, as does the film. It is the opposite of the eclipse; a negativity that is neither radiant nor solar, a failed epiphany.

At first it is nothing, just an observation of his difficulty in making a start: "I need a long time to adapt and settle," he writes to me, "before feeling finally that something becomes necessary and obvious, and the film starts to appear." Then, little by little, the slight initial misunderstanding grows and our flourishing collaboration withers. He is more and more deaf to what I try to say to him, I am more and more blind to what he wants to show me. Here we are, *in opposition*. I am more and more irritated, he is more and more worried. Suddenly, something takes hold, jams, stops. We are no longer inhabiting the same time.

Soon, his nocturnal side reawakes, it takes hold of him. At night, he has palpitations: diastole, systole, he opens himself up and closes over ever more quickly then starts up again, now strangely calm and lucid about his own condition: "you have to be indulgent and pardon my indecisive temperament, my procrastinations, which will always get the better of me." I then understand the effort that it took for him to make *Thierry, portrait d'un absent*, and why this film seems still today, in spite of its painful subject matter and merciless ending, to free itself victoriously from a background of doubt and darkness.

On either side of the friendship, both sides of the bank, in Kyoto and Tokyo, a parallel set-up takes shape. Each one wants to make the film his own way, to his own rhythm, to his own beat. Rhapsody in July: we are tearing each other apart with the calendar as our background. Everything appears uncertain, *faded*, melted like snow. It is the definition of the *fondu*, the fade in the cinema, as an object is replaced gradually by another. A sentiment—friendship—is progressively and almost imperceptibly replaced by another: mistrust. A reversal in the order of the shots: the episodes do not follow on one from the other as planned. Very quickly, the signs of disagreement multiply, the film looks increasingly like a defeat, even a surrender. The denouement is inevitable.

*

No reasoning can ever reassure us of the reality, the existence of a friendship. As is well known, it is only with our friends that we really quarrel. What characterizes friendship is that it can be broken at any time. It is the most fragile, the most tenuous connection—and at the same time, precisely because it at all times involves an *internal* positioning, it is also the most powerful.

I sense the danger in an extraordinarily precise way. What am I to do? It is Montaigne, in his great wisdom, who will give me the key. In a sublime phrase from the *Essais*, he warns against the sudden transformation of friendship into its opposite: "As great friendships are born from great enmities and vigorous health from mortal maladies, it is only a half-turn of the toe to pass from one to the other."

I do not want this film to become a long, shared regret or our friendship, turning in on itself, to veer into a certain kind of rancor or even of detestation. Instead of waiting for our friendship to take a "half-turn of the toe" and become a kind of grudge, I preferred to turn heel. Four weeks after François' arrival at the Villa, I abandon *The Cat's Eye* project for good.

*

François is waiting on the terrace. He is smoking, irritated. He sits on the chair. He lifts his cigarette to his lips. He has smoke in his eyes; he grimaces. He gets up. All I can see now are his chest and the tops of his legs. He remains standing there without knowing really what to do.

A shadow quickly covers his face which he then turns toward the door on the left, his eyes blinking. He lets his arm fall like an injured person tired of being on a drip. With a sad expression, he looks to the air, shakes his head, lowers his eyes. He swings his right hand and I don't know whether it is to flick the ash from his cigarette or in a fatalistic gesture. Both, perhaps.

Then François looks furiously toward the door on the left. The dark curtain on the window is open, allowing a view of the buildings behind the window, outside in the background. The lights finally go out. I close the two shutters on the glass door.

Now, the whole room is plunged into darkness.

*

I have long pondered the reasons for which the project that we had put in place was never realized, rather finally ending with two years of quarreling, then of silence. The answers are many: the difficulties inherent to the project itself; my excessive intransigence, which was the mirror image of his prevarications; and our two strong personalities, which we thought would be combined but which came into conflict with each other.

But there is also something else, something more profound. Firstly, there is the very nature of the relationship between images and words: that is to say, essentially, between cinema and literature. Cinema feeds on words, it devours them. The screenplay of a film does not exist. Or rather it exists only to be pitilessly put into images and swallowed up, definitively sent into the *abyss* in the irruption of cinematographic representation. Entirely coauthors of the project, François and I were in agreement that we would both be its directors, but he had too much experience in cinema and I had too much love for literature for there not to be a replay of the old antagonism of films and books. We dreamed of an impossible thing, perhaps. A book-film, in the limited time of a summer, a *flowering*.

Finally, there is something that we had not thought about and which concerns friendship itself. Friendship does not grow on fusion: it is built across distances. Contrary to the accepted vision of an irresistible force, bolted down and forever locked in, friendship is a certain kind of codified and fragile relationship. Though it might sometimes be dressed up in that way, friendship is neither an association nor a cooperation. And that is why working with a friend is the hardest thing in the world.

Now, more than ten years later, I can put things into perspective. On the calm blankness of paper, I do what I think he would have done: I cut the bone of contention—*shared* faults—in two and in writing this novel, I give the final word to friendship.

*

But it is to François that I must leave the last word. Two years later, in a letter that is just like him, sensitive and modest, he writes to me:

I wanted to reach out to you. Because our quarrel weighs on me. Life does go on and every day we mourn. But when are we capable of repairing what is broken…? For my part, I have decided to make a clean slate of both my criticisms and faults so as not to go back over the good and bad motives that have led us to this point. I needed to let you know so that you might eventually send me a sign in your turn.

I hope you are well.

François

François' letter fills me with an immense happiness. This is what makes friendship so remarkable: you think you know all about it and it suddenly comes up, it takes off again. All real friendship is storm, speed, hurricane, the slippery element of the wind. At that point, all seems once again possible and joyous.

Some years later, on 11 March 2011, at 7.13 a.m. Paris time, as an unprecedented earthquake has just hit Japan, and before even the nuclear emergency is declared at the Fukushima power station, I received a message of support and friendship, the first in a long series. It was from François.

3. THE ADVENTURERS OF SOUND

The two years that followed the failure of the film *In the Cat's Eye* were, to use one of François' own expressions, "some very nasty times."

There is no shortage of various and varied projects, some done to earn a living, others more personal, but none of these come to anything. There are some very unfavorable external and objective circumstances: the economic crisis, budget cuts, the change in the status of casual show-business workers, but also a psychological state that contributes to what can only be described as a rough patch. Something was broken in Japan, not only in his personal life, but also certainly in his relationship with cinema. His very exacting conception of cinema as creation—and not as entertainment—he finds nowhere, or almost nowhere.

One of the few exceptions was, for him, the work of Lars von Trier. He would always have a great admiration for the Danish director, the author of inflammatory and inventive films: *Breaking the Waves* and especially *The Idiots* (his favorite), which seemed to him the most capable, in their radicality, to shake up the "old cinematographic diplodocus." He was immediately sensitive, for example, to the innovative principles set out for the first time by the manifesto *Dogma 95*, on 20 March 1995 in Paris at the Odéon theater during a meeting appropriately entitled "Cinema toward its second century," and which were distributed that evening, in the form of small red tracts, to a dumfounded audience.

What is *Dogma 95*? A manifesto for a new cinema based on a few simple principles: the obligation to film *by hand*, the toning down of the narcissism of the author (the name of the director must not be mentioned), the refusal to be classified by a genre label, the prohibition of simulated actions and optical artifices (sex must have *really* taken place), filming *in situ* and with natural lighting, filters are banned as are additional sound, make-up, importance is placed on improvisation... Finally, the emphasis is on the *here and now* of the action and, more than anything, the ultimate rule—unwritten—which is that you can always depart from the rules. In short, the suspension of all the machinery of globally commoditized dramatic illusion. He saw in this series of experimental counter propositions another means of filming, a salutary reflex in reaction to the mass productions of the film industry and to the control they have over society in order to "break the waves" of conformism and to reinvent cinema.

Ten years later, however, this movement is disbanded and the cinematographic machinery is more omnipotent than ever. The idea of calling into question conventional cinematographic language to initiate a proper reflection on what cinema has become today has fallen away drastically, and the failure of the Japanese film sounded the death knell for his dreams. The cinematic dinosaur was already dead and is now definitively buried: if only we could still dream as high as the grass it trod on.

Yet, the relations between art and the real and knowing how to represent the world to *really* express it are questions that still gnaw away at François. Nourished by his experience with Alain Cavalier and his passion for Lars von Trier, for years he tried to find in cinema a form that would satisfy that experience and passion. Yet paradoxically, it is in quite another register that he would soon begin to give his own singular response. In 2009, a new window opens. A sonic window, he slips into it without hesitating and becomes a director of radio drama shows at France Culture.

*

I have begun my new life at Radio France. It is the upper deck of a circular cruise liner. First class, the sea air, and a lovely clear horizon. I breathe and I am enjoying myself. To have to make a drama per week, more or less, is a change from a film every twelve months at best. No time to think too much, to get anxious... You have to be creative, quick, and be already thinking of the next text... Which gives to the work a lightness that I had never known. It is a busy rate of work but interesting because it remains artisanal.

A *vita nuova*, then. On the "circular cruise liner" of the Radio France building, François little by little opens up again, becomes confident in himself again, discovers new texts and breathes once more the sea air: "I read, I read, I read: I read from morning until the evening, then through the night." Above all, he also meets some impressive people there. Engineers, chief cameramen, technicians, a whole artistic and technical squad dedicated to the sonic crafts and on whom he can rely.

It is the almost invisible world of the radio, the perched people of the antennae and the fine game of the studios, all the animal spirits who transform noise into sound. Thanks to this world, François would have the happiest moments of his creative life. Called "sound production," it is a concrete construction as well as a crowning, a veritable actualization through sound.

At Lakanal, François would listen to the radio all night, alternating with the Bach *Suites* that he played in a loop all through the day. In the next room, I would hear clear trilling sounds all day, while at night there was the crackling of the radio waves. The radio was right next to the bed and he slept with the transistor by his ear, rolled over in coils of sleep and sound. At Radio France, he was to be able to give free rein to his passion as never before.

*

We have to pay homage to the radio people, these adventurers of sound. In those cold, bare-walled rooms, they make the timbres resound and bring colors to life. At the beginning, there is nothing: a round table, chairs, microphones. A few musical instruments, a drum kit, an old harpsichord. A cup of tea, a bottle of water. The walls are covered in strips of wood for the acoustics. You see some headphones lying around, anoraks draped over folders. Placed on the table, a simple white felt-tip with a black cap.

People are around the table, reading, doing their own thing and yet all together. They read, they train their voices, they search for the voice, place it… People are reading round a table and it is very beautiful.

Above the arched heads and shoulders searching for the right intonation hang booms like bamboos tearing up the space; at their extremities are the big black eyes of the seemingly omnipresent microphones. Then, in the middle of the wires, cables, cords, some bags thrown in a pile and stacked up seats, a strange phenomenon occurs: the adventurers are set out in a circle, like for a council, and the miracle happens. They open the world up through sound.

*

The transposition of literary texts to the radio is a vast unknown continent. It is the work of a few madmen who, in response to the planetary reign of the image, offer verbal and sonic guerilla warfare and invite us to follow them on some violent and pleasant incursions into the world of the radio wave. They have a marvelous name, technicians and artists: they are the *metteurs en ondes*, the producers.

They are invisible, they do not go on television, you never

see them on screen. They are not part of a staff, a team, a squad, but make up little mobile, tight-knit bands for whom *listening* is primordial and *harmony* the horizon. They have no baseline and make no conference calls: when they meet, it is round a table. They don't do brainstorming; they work in concert. They are at once their front office, their middle office, and their back office, passing from one to the other by voice in a few meters as easily as if they were drinking a glass of water. They are not very "must have" or even less "insight," and the radio is their life and not a "means of communication." Finally, they have their own particular way of creating and a specific savoir-faire: they know each other in sonic signals, in electric currents, in sensitive membranes and in magnetic plates, in desks and in tracks, in digital consoles. The *nec plus ultra*: they know exactly where to place a microphone.

It is not for nothing that they speak of *prise de son*, catching sound, recording it: something vibrates in the air and you need to know how to catch it. Capture it but also let it go again. Grab it but also let it spread. Confine it but also liberate it. Let it unfurl. Radio is a hold-up, a burglary. It is the art of catching.

A text, some voices, that's all. And a place as well as a technique—some even say a *spirit*—that links them: the radio.

There is a knowledge of sound, a gigantic portable encyclopedia that is lodged between the bronchi and the lungs. It is an internal treasure, an ancestral depot, built up from age to age. There is also the unlimited reservoir of the sounds of nature, the *stock*, and it is a question of being sensitive to it and then of knowing how to use it. Here, the inventiveness of the geniuses of sound is without limits: they play on the fabrics, the materials, the textiles, the textures. Sound can do everything and all you need is to know how to use it. With a window and some sponges, you create the impression of cars arriving very quickly, skidding—the magic passes. Danger, fear? It is a large steel leaf that trembles. With a bucket of water and a rope, they create the sounds of a rescue. The smells, the colors and sounds work together: like in particle physics, you situate yourself always on the margins of the keenest forms of knowledge and of the most insane experimentation.

In Studio 110, with some ends of rope, some wire-strainers and cables, they improvise the invisible. Everything, absolutely everything, the world of sound recreates everything, far beyond that which can be spoken. It is the immense power of the radio, its benevolent supremacy, its omniscient royalty, the whole universe at its knees, sky, night, globe, spheres, galaxies, under the scepter of the microphone, as fragile as a reed.

*

François sometimes works alone, sometimes in twos or threes... He may also have under his direction some actors, up to fifty or so for a series. On the radio, actors have no more need of the image and are no longer held under its yoke so they can concentrate on something else: the barely perceptible, the delicate, the subtle, the vital. The true. They get back to what is impalpable but indispensable, elementary but essential: the attention placed on a cesura, an intonation, the importance of breathing.

Taking the timber from a phrase, muffling it. Placing a note where it should be, knowing how to bring out an onomatopoeia. A phrase, a single one, can take on different accents, modulations that are so different that the whole system of meaning can be suddenly overturned.

*

Sometimes, however, things get stuck, blocked, falter.

As musicians know well, sound demands an extraordinary capacity of concentration in order to reproduce it faithfully. His head in his hands, his mouth pinched, François concentrates intensely. He absents himself, absorbs himself in the heavy silence of sound, in the work of voices, the depths from which they emerge. His hand on his brow, always: the brow indicates pressure, the barometer of anxiety. It is the electric line that registers his feelings: it rises, it falls, he is worried, tormented. You need some tension, a precise distribution of the accents, a balanced arrangement of the pauses, a clear distribution of the volumes… Radio: searching for precision at all times. "A tad more. A tad closer still," he says, furrowing his brow, of course. He is right: everything plays out on a razor's edge.

It is a sonic sprint. The takes follow one after the other at an incredible speed: you rarely see people work at that speed. The studio is at boiling point.

The effort is at its peak. You need to direct the actors, say when it works, when it works less well, when it does not work. Humor has an important role. You play with people's voices, even with the deepest, most intimate, most precious parts of them… the most fragile, too. The slightest misstep can bring down the whole edifice of the recording. A false note and confidence goes, you fall into morose, stiff, or forced declamations. François gives his ideas, intuitions, advice, and you feel he empathizes with his actors, that he is supporting them as much as he is pulling them along.

With their two large black heads perched at the end of long stems, the microphones are homing devices. Monstrous beasts for an enchanted result. They track sound, breathing and, through them, the most difficult thing to capture: emotion.

The position of the body is very important. In a recording

studio, the slightest noise takes on an unusual importance. Everything becomes at once very sensitive: the temperature of the bodies, the fluids, the moods... Someone sniffs and it's a whole issue. Someone touches their nose or their hair with their hand and the slightest gesture takes on an unsuspected meaning. It is the whole great internal ballet of particles playing out which suggests itself, which expectorates itself.

Recording sound is like taking blood for a fundamental transfusion. It comes from very far and goes back through the centuries to the beginnings of time. "You have to see it to believe it," as they say. No, you have to hear it to believe it, and you have to believe it to hear it, every sound and every gesture take on suddenly a reversible importance. We then understand from which obscure dreams we are made, from which sensitive, delicate, gossamer-thin material, we are woven.

*

Finally, there is the editing. If recording is a sprint, editing is a marathon. The radio producer, like the writer, works at the editing table. You need passion and patience. The variety of contents must correspond to that of the sound processing options. According to the place (interior, exterior), to the desired effects, to the rhythm of the text, they will pursue the best arrangement across the infinite variety of possibilities in calibrating the sound. Editing cells are like gray cells. It is the very work of intelligence.

The choice of music will, of course, be crucial. In this, François has a great time, working *to his heart's content*: luth, oboe, piano, harpsichord, flute, sometimes even a symphonic orchestra. He creates a veritable complex organism of timbres and tonalities, of words and silences. It is a *lecture* in the fullest sense of the term.

And then everything disappears, the sound vanishes. The actors go home, the technicians tidy the cables, the engineers leave the turntable. The pretty blonde actress puts her coat back on and turns up her collar, everyone leaves: the show vanishes into thin air waiting for its resurrection, presently through the airwaves, across the world. You would almost believe it was a dream, that nothing had happened. You find yourself alone, in the quiet and in the night.

*

Recording: 15 days.
Editing: 30 days.
Mixing: 2 days per episode.
Normally between 15 and 20 days.

There are, of course, accidents, some problems, some improvisations, but so that the latter may come precisely, everything needs to be timed, regulated, and *go like clockwork.* Sometimes, you come out of the studio, go into the street, you become the ear of a car park, a bypass, a wheat field. Then, when a scene goes well, when an atmosphere works, when a text breathes under the skin, through rhythm, through the body, through the voice, when the recording is right, you can hear François get up, enthused: "We have it! We have it, we have it, we have it! It is perfect!"

*

Homage to radio. Radio is a queen.

Radio practically saved François' life, it allowed him to find himself again in his relationship with art and in his relations with other people. But he gave back a hundredfold: his radio recordings are most often lively, precise, bright. Some of them are little jewels to listen to, living mosaics where his style can immediately be found, his voice among all the other voices. He almost managed to create a new genre: *the sonic film*.

But apart from their intrinsic quality and the ever-renewing array of readings they propose, what interests me in François' radio works is that they reveal one of the essential points of our friendship and beyond that, I believe, of all friendship.

François was a man who listened. He knew how to open his ear, and that is why he could incite the deepest affection. For friendship is nothing but that: a listening. The opening up to a pulsation, a vibration. Or to put it even more concretely: a tightrope between beings, fragile, fine, tenacious, that crosses over the abyss and is supported by nothing.

4. LA GRACIOSA

Now I see the shadows run across the stone walls. The wind makes the building crack. On the slate roof the shadow of the night slides. A sheet of paper crosses the room, enters by one door and leaves by another, blown by the wind. On the balcony across the street, I can see some clothes drying on a washing line. That is all that remains most often, at the end: shadows, clothes.

*

Thursday 26 December on the island of La Graciosa, in the Canary Islands.

La Graciosa is well named, it is an enchantment. How many times did François talk to me about it? "Graciosa the gracious," "Graciosa the divine grace," "the aptly named Graciosa, that little pebble in the Canaries": he had fallen in love with this little slither of sand and rock, eight kilometers long and four wide, far from the crowds of tourists, tucked away in the immensity of the tides. He goes there regularly to "fill up on iodine, trade winds, sun, and even rain." He did not know that, each time, it was his own death that he was speaking about.

On La Graciosa there is a village, a port, a few beaches, and nothing else. No paved roads, just sand. No pollution: motor vehicles are banned, without exception. The number of restaurants can be counted on the fingers of one hand. They drink there an elegant and light little red wine. Fish there is always served fresh.

La Graciosa: summer seems to reign permanently in these parts. When the weather is clear and the wind doesn't blow too hard, the sea is like a river and the day is pleasant, with beautiful skies embroidered with white clouds whose trails fill François with wonder. The water and the waves play with each other in a thousand ways. And the nights are even more beautiful.

The entirety of these lands emerging in a murmuring of foam at the crest of the waters forms a landscape of an almost supernatural beauty. Watch out, however: around the island, the currents are powerful and most often unpredictable, they change according to the underwater relief and the force and direction of the winds. The sea can be calm and soft, then suddenly rough. The drift currents often run parallel to the shore. Most of the time, when you go to swim, you don't come out of the water at the same place you went in.

*

I have investigated, done my research, I have tried to understand.

We sometimes think, wrongly, that waves are created by

tides. In reality it is with the wind that they begin. The swell first forms out at sea. The larger the surface over which the wind blows without meeting any obstacles, the higher the waves are. When the wave approaches the coastlines, the depth of the water changes again its profile: the steeper the underwater slope, the bigger it will be. Then, everything becomes horribly simple: the wave approaches the shore, its curvature grows, the height of the crest increases, the water tips forward, and the wave unfurls.

The beach of Las Conchas, where Bahia and François were to lose their lives, is one of the most beautiful in the world. But it is also one of the most isolated, on the other side from the little port of Caleta de Sebo, the only access point to the island. Almost directly facing it is Montaña Clara island and, farther still, Alegranza island, where thousands of seabirds glide over a magnificent caldera. The positioning of the islands creates zones of acceleration where the wind is channeled between the Los Riscos mountain chain and the island of La Graciosa. The "strong southeasterly" in particular is a formidable wind: it blows at all hours and unties anchors, the sea quivers and rises up at its approach, whilst whirls of foam form very quickly on the tops of the waves. It is untamable: you don't sense it approaching, you can never know when it begins to blow, and it falls as quickly as it rises up.

Far out to sea, waves are formed. They are made up of the incessant superimposition of a multitude of elementary waves. It is infinity in action, supple and mobile, liquid. The waves accumulate and overlap in an irrepressible whinnying of foam, they pass at every instant under each other in an inexhaustible and random combination, they are covered by other waves or rise up in layers, they interfere with and threaten each other, they join up and separate in an incessant turbulence that is the very movement of life.

The formation of the waves, their frequency, their violence, their amplitude: it is one of the domains where the science is the least certain. I imagine, cruel irony, how much that would have interested you, you who spent your time in history and science books and who called one of your films *Surprises of Matter*. They often use physical models to understand waves, founded on the mechanics of fluids. But scientists today go so far as to say that certain waves follow the rules of quantum mechanics, described by Schrödinger's famous nonlinear equation which we spoke about so much. Sea waves would not propagate themselves in a linear fashion, but rather it would seem that the waves interact, the largest taking the energy from the smallest. One thing is certain: they end up forming a whole whose violence is far greater than the sum of its parts.

In a facile way, the sea gives us the impression of a certitude, a unity: the seascape is an image, stable, protected from fractures by the shine of the postcard or the screen. The sea refuses nothing, excludes no one. It is the ideal image of the relationship between the world and us. A sort of pure present, marvelous, shimmering. But in its deepest meaning, it is a savage trough and its murmurings go far beyond our comprehension.

*

Thursday 26 December of a year that no longer exists. I think of the sea and I think of the wind. I look through the news, the photos, the maps, the letters that come back to me like wreckage washed onto the shore by the ocean.

I would have liked to have thought that François' departure in this paradisiacal place had some beauty to it, the sea and the sand, the sun spinning—but I know he wanted to survive and, above all, that he thought of Bahia right to the end. I imagine his anguish and say to myself but that it is a terrible, absurd death. Then, a bitter wind blows across the marram grass and my memory rears up: the wave crashes again, pitiless.

That morning, there are some clouds. It is not too hot but it is very windy. Everything happens very quickly: a single wave, brutal and inexplicable, will suffice. On the beach at Las Conchas, though they were doing nothing but walking, the wave harpoons them and they quickly cross the liquid mirror. To them, it lasts a century, though it is only a second. Then everything happens at a prodigious speed. They are carried out to sea and the world falls away infinitely.

The sea, that prodigious mass of water… But where is the flickering shoreline? The strait changed so suddenly. What can you do against the sea? You need to wait for the swell to abate, you need to wait for a boat to come. But the sea takes its time. An immense patience of water, salt, and seaweed, a device for contemplating time.

Soon, everything takes on the density of stone. The sea is hostile, the light of winter makes them feel distress and cold. They are little by little overtaken by the incomprehensible. It is a vast liquid country that opens up under their feet. A formidable power pulls them toward the bottom, the circle of the eclipse closes slowly, the world dissipates in an odor of salt and the cries of the birds. It is the end of the roll, the revenge of the liquid pathway, the window closes over. Now, there is no longer childhood or memory. Now, there are no more fishermen on the sea. Now, it is the end even of silence.

Death is a chilling and powerful text and fear comes always too late. Above the uninterrupted swell of the Canaries, the seagulls are fixed in the skies. They beat their wings, immobile. How long it lasted, I don't want to imagine as it does not belong to the time of things that happen. I am already at the limit, the moment approaches where I too will not be able to go any farther. Now, I can be with them only at this precise instant of the narration and hold it as softly, as lovingly as I can, at any cost, to envelop them in a phrase, the most tender possible, a punctuated piece of clothing where floats one final time their smile, to give back to them a little of that open air and that warmth that at that moment they so lacked.

It has come to me, as no doubt to all those close to them, to dream, to roam around in the pain, to imagine another way for the events to work out… François that morning would not have wanted to go to the beach: "Listen, Sylvia, I have some work to do," or Bahia would have caught a cold and stayed in bed, an unexpected phone call would have knocked them off course, they would not have passed by at that precise time and at that specific place… But no. You can't go back. You can't rewind the film or redo the take. Terrible are the things when they emerge outside of themselves, it is the depths of the real that suddenly lifts up and surges towards you.

At 12.25 p.m., a coastguard helicopter is sent to the site, but it is already too late. A boat will pick up the two adolescents who were accompanying them and were themselves carried away by the wave—two miracle survivors, the only good news of that day—but no one could do anything to save François and Bahia.

*

On 11 December 2013, François posted his last public message on Facebook. He would give a few more pieces of news by private messaging, but it is the last phrase that he would write for his friends across the world. Here is that phrase:

"The last one is always the best. I wish a good trip to the flaneurs."

This "last one" is actually the sixth—and last—episode of a series entitled "Geography of the poem." It is dedicated to a little publishing house called La Passe du vent. It is the last show recorded by François.

*

That night, I had a dream. I am walking with François in a vast plain toward a white fence. A bluish wind brushes past our heads. The sky is covered, but an abnormally powerful light illuminates the whole plain and we can see into the distance in the smallest detail. In the background are prairies and villages, a church that falls farther away, fields as far as the eye can see. On the other side there is the sea, reefs, and what looks like a beach. The white fence is at the edge of the beach. As far as the eye can see, all there is is that sea and that beach. The landscape seems to have reached an end point, to be situated in a remoteness that could neither broaden nor recede, neither extend nor unravel.

It is snowing. The blue wind becomes white and the powder covers the landscape. Snowflakes fall thickly and the wind blows them everywhere. The temperature drops. The snow progressively fills the whole sky and soon you can make out neither the fields nor the beach. Everything is cold. There is a painter by the fence. He is working, he is making a portrait of François, but the painting does not look like him: you might say it was a poor imitation, banal and dull, of the real François with his lively gestures and his darting look, his big pianist hands that flutter, masterful in all his variations. Progressively, mysteriously, however, the second François, the one in the portrait, ends up looking like the first.

Arriving as if I am floating at this point of my dream, I touch François' arm: the temperature of his skin has slowly become like that of the snow. I can no longer hear him, can no longer reach him, as the sound of the piano fades away at the moment where the ear can no longer capture it. He is completely immobile.

You could say that between the two François there is nothing left but the thinness of a sheet of cigarette paper and that the more the time passes, the more the François of the portrait catches up with the other, like a peloton catches up with a cyclist in a breakaway. The real face of François does not disappear completely, but it becomes its portrait, it becomes something else while remaining a face. At the instant, now imminent, where they will coincide to make only one face, time will abruptly stop, François will be alone at the summit of his trajectory and the book will be finished.

5. THE CHAOTIC GALLERIES

The window opens. From here I can see the former quarries of Montmartre, now filled in and covered with houses, buildings, bars, little private gardens, public squares, restaurants, even vineyards. Montmartre was developed in this way, on the margins, outside of the initial perimeter of the city, pushing its astonishing blossoming far from the beaten track, pushing and growing the capital outside of itself, to the periphery.

This part of Paris is built over an enormous empty space: in the 18th century, alongside the extension of the city toward the north and west, new buildings began to be built at the very site where marl, slate, clay and most notably the famous fine plaster of Paris, which they call the "Parisian white" were extracted. The quarries: those vast underwater amphitheaters, made up of some three hundred kilometers of galleries of stone and sand, had already given up from the earth the material used to construct a large part of the city of Paris. But soon, it was this worksite itself that would be covered over so that the development of Paris could continue.

Louis-Sébastien Mercier tells of the scene in his *Tableau de Paris*, in 1781: "With Paris growing bigger, they have imperceptibly built faubourgs on the former quarries; so that all you see on the outside is essentially missing from the ground in the foundations of the city: hence the frightening cavities that are found today below the houses in many districts. They sit on top of abysses… When you see cracks on them, and when you think about what lies underneath the ground in part of this superb city, a secret shiver takes hold of you… And people drink, eat, and sleep in the buildings that stand on this uncertain surface."

Few people know it, but it is here that the fossilized bones were discovered that helped Cuvier create paleontology, the scientific discipline that studies fossilized remains of living things. I am passionate about paleontology. In the old books, it was described very simply as the "science studying ancient life"; it is so to speak a systematic study of disappearance. But one often forgets to say that it uses this analysis of the past to interrogate the evolutionary implications of these remains. In this sense, paleontology is not at all a backward-looking or out of date discipline, on the contrary: in each fossil, there is a salvation to come.

Our lives are built on chaotic galleries. Down below walls, terraces and mounds are to be found, a whole subterranean city where roads, crossroads, staircases are cut into the stone, uneven and often poorly laid-out squares. Sometimes, fallen rocks over several hectares, four to five meters deep! This is what is known as the "chaotic galleries."

And it is from these galleries that both ragged walls and majestic stone columns are born and raised. From these deep, distant rivers the most beautiful waterfalls can flourish: vertical wells and damp passageways lead you to wide avenues where the sun spreads in yellow glimmers, while friends on the terraces play cards, drink wine and laugh gently. These are underground arenas, obscure cavities, sparkling geodes from which surface the bright colors of evening dresses, the blue or pink shawls covering the shoulders and caressing the arms, necklaces made from seashell or jade over low-cut dresses, all of which rises up from the crumbling of these enigmatic structures falling into dust.

*

In the end I found it, the grave. In Montmartre cemetery, three years later on 14th August, in the middle of summer.

François and Bahia's tomb is in the 6th division, Ledoux path, between the Avenue des Carrières and the Rue de la Barrière-Blanche. This path, probably the least visited in the cemetery, opens up a side passageway off the Avenue du Tunnel. The gravel, thicker here in this rarely visited part, crunches beneath my feet.

The grave is beautiful. It is the work of Mozart Guerra, a Brazilian sculptor, a friend. It is not only a grave, but an immense white stone which is tilted, sloping gently skyward, and covered with a concrete plaque inlaid with hundreds of multicolored marbles that belonged to François and Bahia, like a supernova. A rain of red, blue, green, quartz, agate, salmon marbles—set at the time of the stone's fabrication in the churning concrete and which, curiously, seem now to spurt out of the material itself in a strange, inverted emulsion, a crackling of childhood rediscovered.

Sparkling; a polyphony of stone. With its gently leaning surface and its marbles like scattered pearls, the grave conceptualized by Mozart Guerra is not a grave: it is a rocket, a prototype. A polychromatic catapult, ready to launch. The intelligence of this grave is that it is the opposite of a grave. It is not directed downward, but rises up. Mozart has understood not to search for commemoration, but to find again the life force.

To have a friend is a wonderful thing. The friend is a "rare pearl, a demi-god." Maybe Cicero is exaggerating, but he does have a point. The friend is rarity itself. Friendship is a *monumental* event in the life of a human being but this monument is not immobile and absent, hidden away in some cemetery, it is nomadic and scintillating. It is a portable blaze; you carry it with you at all times.

Today's cemeteries, with their paths and alleyways, the walkways planted with cypress trees, are places reserved for the dead, where there is nothing to do except pay them a visit. Our relationship with death has become decorative, landscaped, touristic. It was not always thus and, in other places, they keep the memory—I was going to say the secret—of a different topography, thought of not only in relation to death, but from the perspective of the living. In Japan, at the time when the cherry trees blossom, people go to the graves to celebrate: they set up between the gravestones, spread out a blue rug on the grass, then they drink some sake and eat some grilled chicken, and recite poems as they watch the petals take flight. In Madagascar, they turn the body over, wrap it in a fresh cloth and make it dance round the tomb before sending it back in there. In China, they set off firecrackers and burn banknotes!

As for me, more humbly, I place here this book so that another picks it up and takes it farther still: a way of keeping you both alive, of making you exist still in the waves of time.

*

Now, I lift you out of the abyss of time. I evoke you, invoke you, expose you. I fix you, I look at you and fix you at once, forever, on paper. Yet, I feel peaceful: if I have done things well, you will be able to escape.

I draw you and I trace you. I tow you, extract you. I pull you out from the dark depths where you lie, sunken.

I reply silently to your silent call. I draw a line under all that has separated us.

I trace you, portray you. A book is finally nothing other than a way of saying: wherever you may be, I will be there. So long as I can, I will carry you.

*

I set the book down on the stone, and now I must return. I move forward, I go back down the paths, I make my way between the graves… I myself inhabit this land of tombs and, by a different path, I get back to the top of the mound, where my house is.

CODA

It is now four years since François died, a little before the end of the year. Since then, I have looked from time to time in an envelope on my desk, at the only photo of him with his daughter that I have kept.

At the first light of dawn, I slide open the shutters. I light a stick of incense from the flame of a candle whose trembling glow, faintly lighting up the image of my friend, now makes tangible the infinite distance that separates me from him. The rays from the candle do not light up directly the faces in the photograph, but in the half-light that bathes the room, the contours of their black volume stand out even more clearly than in broad daylight. It is like a shadowy density that, each morning, devours each one of their features a little more.

I turn away from the photo and try to remember François' face in the dawn light. The lines of his face become blurred, his look escapes me, then his eyebrows, then lastly his smile erases itself. And yet, the memory of François does not decrease inside me. The white powder of the gypsum rises up from the quarries. The more time passes the more I remember everything.

There are all sorts of whites. There is a dreadful white, a dirty white, the terrible white of the cadaver and of the sheet that covers it. The pale and wan white of ruptures, the pallid white of treacheries. But white is not a unitary, homogenous color. White is not even a color, but the condition of all color, light personified. There are all kinds of whites. There is the faintly blue white that rises in the morning from the trees in the Parc de Sceaux. There is the pinky white of the dawn on the walls of the Lycée Lakanal or on the slopes of the Montmartre cemetery. The white of the window, immaculate and colorless, that you press against to breathe a little fresh air and to look at the birds flying in the pure white sky. The chalky white of Corsica, of cheeses and of fresh butter, the white of peaches and of the vine, the Semillon, the Muscadelle, the Entre-Deux-Mers, the white Merlot. There is the diffuse white of dark theaters, the silvery white of the big screen when Hitchcock invades it, pierces it at the same time. The toubab white of Senegal, the ivory white of the piano, the platinum white of the radio, the effervescent white of the studios. The champagne white of Bahia, lilium white, lily perfume, and the white of the blank page where your story will now be inscribed, while on a branch of the nearby tree, drawn by the seeds and the fruits, two blue tits have come to rest.